KINDERGARTEN STORIES

AND

MORNING TALKS

WITH OVER 125 ILLUSTRATIONS

ORIGINAL TEXT WRITTEN AND COMPILED
BY
SARA E. WILTSE

EDITED BY
TIMOTHY FRANK

CARDAMOM PUBLISHERS
JANESVILLE, WI

Cover illustration: The Three Tom Boys (by J.G. Brown—1868).

Title page illustration: New England School-House
(Prang & Co. — date unknown).

Kindergarten Stories and Morning Talks With Over 125 Illustrations
Copyright © 2010 Timothy Frank/Cardamom Publishers
All rights reserved

Published by
Cardamom Publishers
P.O. Box 2146
Janesville, WI 53547

Printed in the United States of America

ISBN 978-0-9742181-4-4
Library of Congress Control Number: 2010921733
Library of Congress Subject Heading: 1. Children's stories. 2. Short stories.
3. Home schooling. 4. Fairy tales.
5. Education--Curricula--United States--Juvenile literature.

Original Text Published by Ginn & Company 1894
Copyright 1890 by Sara E. Wiltse

INTRODUCTION.

I CORDIALLY recommend this collection of simple object lessons and stories which Miss Wiltse has arranged for the Kindergarten. Their value will depend on the way in which they are brought before the children. The salient points of both should be studied before they are presented to the children, that they may be given in a spirited manner.

LALIAH B. PINGREE.

PREFACE.

THIS collection of stories is intended for a series of texts upon which the teacher may elaborate.

Great liberty has been taken in revising, and it is expected that experienced story-tellers will adapt, lengthen, shorten, or remake, as the needs of their pupils demand.

More material has usually been given for each week than can be used, but a kindergartner will be able to select from it that which is suited to the different grades in her room.

Thanks are due the authors who have kindly permitted such use of their work, and to the *Christian Register, Christian Union,* and *Independent* for stories which first appeared in their columns.

Miss Phelps' poem, "A Hebrew Legend," is published by permission of and arrangement with Messrs. Houghton, Mifflin, & Co.

Roberts Brothers kindly allow the use of Dr. E. E. Hale's story of "Our Daily Bread"; and Fords, Howard, & Hulburt permit the selection from Rev. Henry Ward Beecher's "Norwood." These courtesies are gratefully acknowledged by the

EDITOR.

CONTENTS.

ILLUSTRATIONS.

———❦———

The New School-Mistress.
Drawn by Miss Jennie Brownscombe, 1873.

FIRST WEEK OF SEPTEMBER.

LEAD the children to tell something about their homes and who keeps them tidy, bringing out the mother-care in the family. Draw attention to young birds fed by the mother-bird. Stimulate observation of the birds and their feather dresses; of lambs and their covering of wool. Question about the children's clothes and the material of which they are made, dwelling upon the fact that for much of our clothing we are indebted to the sheep. Show pictures of sheep if there is no opportunity for the children to see live ones, and tell how the wool is sheared every spring.

Give a brief sketch of the process by which a kindergarten ball is produced. A simple game helps to deepen the impression of our indebtedness to the sheep. One child takes a kindergarten ball, another a blackboard eraser of wool, and a third a pair of wool hose. The others then ask: —

> "Baa, baa, little sheep,
> Have you any wool?"

And the three answer: —

> "Yes; we have three bags full, —
> One for the eraser, and one for the ball,
> And one which we make into stockings for all."

Holding up the three articles as they are mentioned.

Mary and her Lamb may be paraphrased, and in some kindergartens dramatized. Miss Poulson's Finger Song about the lambs may be recited by the teacher.

The Meadow In Springtime.
Published by Currier & Ives, 1867.

MARY HAD A LITTLE LAMB.

Mary had one little lamb. Mary's father had a hundred little lambs. Mary's lamb could not stay in the house with her all of the time; it stayed out in the meadow, with the other little lambs and sheep, most of the time. When Mary went to look at all the lambs playing together, she could not tell surely which was her own until she called, "Pet, Pet!" As soon as she spoke, her lamb would come bounding toward her, and would go with her wherever she went. When she had to go home to go to bed, she would shut the gate between her and her lamb, and then kiss the lamb's woolly head through the bars, telling him, "Good night; be sure to be awake when

Daisy.

From *Golden Moments* by Anonymous.

I go to school in the morning." A part of Mary's path to school was beside the meadow, and the lamb always went as far as he could with her; when she turned the corner so he could go no further, he always put his head through the fence for Mary to give him a good-by hug and a kiss, and as long as he could see her he would cry "baa, baa" ; but when she was quite out of sight, he would go to play with the other lambs, no doubt thinking that a hundred lambs were almost as good playfellows as one little girl.

One day all the sheep were taken from the meadow and driven down the road past the schoolhouse, the lambs being left alone. Mary was afraid something might happen to her lamb, left with so many frisky little creatures without a mother-sheep to tell them not to turn heels over head. Mary's father had told her she might bring her lamb down past the schoolhouse at noon and see what they were doing with the old sheep; so Mary let the lamb follow her to school in the morning, though her father did not mean she should do so. It really was no harm, and I am sorry "it made the children laugh and play," so that the teacher had to turn the lamb out of doors. But just as soon as school closed, Mary ran out, and hugging the woolly little lamb, said, "You dear, patient little Pet! now we will take a walk"; and away they went down the road toward the river. Very soon they heard all sorts of baas, — big, coarse baas, pretty, soft baas, and coarse and soft baas all mingled together. [Children can easily produce the sound.]

It was a strange sight that Mary and Pet saw. Some men were carrying the sheep into the water and were washing their warm woolly coats in the clear, cool river. Mary asked her father if she might wash her lamb, and her father said she might wash his face and see how he liked that. Mary took off her shoes and stockings and waded into the water. Mary's lamb splashed in after her, and when his face had been neatly washed, Mary's father said the clay was so warm that she might wash all of her lamb's wool. What fun they had! The lamb enjoyed it quite as much as Mary did. Mary was afraid the dust would get into the damp wool and make her lamb look more untidy than if he had not been washed, so she took off her apron, and putting the lamb's fore-legs through the sleeves, started home; but the lamb would not stir a step while dressed in that way, and Mary took the sleeves off his legs and tied them in a pretty bow-knot under his chin; this seemed to please him much better, for he now trotted briskly ahead of her a part of the way home. I wish you had been at that schoolhouse when Mary and her lamb went past the teacher and all the children were eating their luncheon out under the trees, and they laughed as you or I would laugh, to see a lamb dressed in a girl's apron.

When all the old sheep had been in the sunny meadow a few days after their bath in the river, their thick coats of wool had become quite dry, and they were taken to the barn, where the farmers cut off their wool every summer. Mary and her lamb went too. Mary said her lamb ought to be taught to keep very quiet while being sheared, and her father said the best-behaved lambs always made the best sheep; so Mary taught her lamb to keep its feet quite still while she played that she cut its wool all off to make herself a dress. Some of the wool from a mother-sheep was made into a ball for Mary to hang round Pet's neck so she could tell him from the other lambs, and Mary had a dress, a hood, a pair of mittens, and some stockings made from the wool that was cut from the sheep's backs that day. Mary took a pair of scissors and clipped a tiny lock of wool from Pet's back, and tying it with a blue ribbon, put it in a box marked: "Pet's first wool; washed and cut off by Mary."

[The story of the Bramble Bush admirably connects bird life with the sheep, and suggests the interdependence of animals.]

THE BRAMBLE BUSH AND THE LAMBS.

Once there was a little brook where the horses and cows and sheep used to go to drink. On the banks of the brook sweet flowers grew, and there were many bramble bushes there also; when the sheep ran down to the water, the brambles caught hold of their wool and often pulled out little white shreds of it, that made the bushes look as if they had white flowers. The sheep did not like having their wool torn off in this manner, and they often complained of the brambles, saying they had no use for wool, and ought not to take it. The sheep said, "We are quite willing to let the farmers shear every lock of wool from our backs; for it is then made into stockings, and dresses, and — [let the children name things made of wool]. We think these bramble bushes of no use in the world; the cows who drink from the brook with us give their milk to the children, the horses draw carriages and carts, but what kindness did a bramble bush ever do?" The bramble bushes said not a word, but held the bits of white wool on the tips of their sharp little fingers.

The Bramble Bush and The Lambs.
From *The Summers Readers First Reader*
by Maud Summers, 1908.

When the sun rose one sweet spring morning, and the sheep were still lying in the grassy meadow not far from the bramble bushes, they heard a beautiful song overhead; it was a bird, just arrived from the sunny South, singing his glad thanks for the new day, and for his dear nest which he had left in a tree when he went away in the autumn. After the song the birds talked in bird language about the nest, which needed a new lining, and as they flew to the brook for their morning bath, what do you think they saw? The bits of wool on the brambles. And the sheep heard them talking as they worked, of the kindness of the brambles in gathering the wool for them; and the sheep looked more kindly upon the bramble bushes after that, and sometimes pushed their woolly heads into the bushes to give them a fresh bit for other birds.

Anonymous.

Canaries and Nest.
From *Ornithological Dictionary Of British Birds* by George Montagu, 1831.

American Robin or Migratory Thrush.
From *The Birds of America, from Drawings Made in Their Territories.*
By John James Audubon, 1841.

SECOND WEEK OF SEPTEMBER.

HAVE you seen any birds this week? What have you seen them doing? Aren't they little creatures?

[Children love dearly to observe little animals, and the teacher should dwell somewhat upon the helplessness of young creatures and the great care which all mothers bestow upon the young. Attention may be drawn to the bathing of birds, the cleanliness of kittens, and the fondness of lambs for clean, grassy places. The children may be questioned about what the birds and lambs and kittens wear, and what the lambs give to the children; what the baby at home wears that the sheep supplies, and what the children's mothers are doing for them while they are in kindergarten.]

STORY OF BIRDS AND FISH.

Three little birds lived in a nest in a tree; the tree stood near the fountain in the Public Garden in Boston, and in the fountain basin lived three little goldfish. One morning the three little birds hopped from their nest and flew down beside the fountain where they spied the three little goldfish. The birds hopped up on the edge of the stone basin and looked at the fish, and the fish swam close to the birds and looked at them.

At last the largest fish said to the smallest bird: —

A bird perched on a branch with blossoms above a fish in a pond.
Japanese woodcut.

"Will you please come into the water and play with us? It is very cool and pleasant here, and if you do not know how to swim, you can run around on the bottom of the basin until we can teach you; it is very easy to swim — for fish at least."

The bird said: —

"We cannot go in water as deep as that in the basin: our wings are not made for swimming, but I see you have something on your sides that looks like tiny wings; perhaps you can fly a little. If you will come out of the water, we will try to teach you to fly from branch to branch of our tree, which I am sure is pleasanter than to stay so much in the water."

But the fish explained that the little things on his sides were fins for swimming, and would never be wings. Just then the mamma-bird called "tweet, tweet," and the three little birds bade the fishes good by, and flew away to see what their mamma wanted.

Just as they reached the home nest, a little boy with his mother came to see the goldfish, and he asked her why the fish kept under water while the birds flew about in the air. His mother told him that fish were so made that they could breathe under water, but birds could only breathe in the air, though a few of them can dive under water for a short time.

The little boy said he was glad he had hands and arms instead of fins or wings, and the little birds told their mamma they were happy as happy could be because they could fly about among the branches of the trees and rest upon flower-stalks; and the little fishes agreed they were very glad to be able to live in the cool water, and swim about, which seemed to them much easier than flying in the dry hot air.

No doubt the Good Friend who takes care of birds, fish, and boys was very glad to see them all so contented.

Miss Wiltse taught a kindergarten many years in Boston, and most of her stories in this book were made for and told to the little children in the Cottage Place Kindergarten.

THIRD WEEK OF SEPTEMBER.

DID you ever go away in the steam cars or in a steamboat? How long did you stay? What did you do for a clean dress or a clean apron while you were gone? Somebody we know is going to take a journey soon. A great number of our little friends are going to a warmer country. But they are not going in the cars, nor in a boat. No; nor in a carriage, nor in the horse cars! Hundreds of them will go together, and not one of them will take a trunk or even a lunch-basket!

Mr. and Mrs. Robin Redbreast, with all their children; Mr. and Mrs. Bluebird, with all their children; Mr. and Mrs. Thrush, with their children, and scores of their cousins; Mr. and Mrs. Blackbird, and all the little Blackbirds; and many a bird that you have not seen or heard this year, will soon fly away to the warm country where they will find green leaves and bright flowers even at Christmas time. Some birds will stay with us. The Pigeons will not go away, nor will the Sparrows go; and if you could go into the woods where many trees grow, you would find the Crows and the Blue Jays even in midwinter.

Little Bird's Nest.
1879.

COMING AND GOING.

There came to our fields a pair of birds that had never built a nest nor seen a winter. How beautiful was everything! The fields were full of flowers, and the grass was growing tall, and the bees were humming everywhere. Then one of the birds began singing, and the other bird said, "Who told you to sing?" And he answered, "The flowers told me, and the bees told me, and the winds and leaves told me, and the blue sky told me, and you told me to sing." Then his mate answered, "When did I tell you to sing?" And he said, "Every time you brought in tender grass for the nest, and every time your soft wings fluttered off again for hair and feathers to line the nest." Then his mate said, "What are you singing about?" And he answered, "I am singing about everything and nothing. It is because I am so happy that I sing."

By and by five little speckled eggs were in the nest, and his mate said, "Is there anything in all the world as pretty as my eggs?" Then they both looked down on some people that were passing by and pitied them because they were not birds.

In a week or two, one day, when the father-bird came home, the mother-bird said, "Oh, what do you think has happened?" "What?" "One of my eggs has been peeping and moving!" Pretty soon another egg moved under her feathers, and then another and another, till five little birds were hatched! Now the father-bird sang louder and louder than ever. The mother-bird, too, wanted to sing, but she had no time, and so she turned her song into work. So hungry were these little birds that it kept both parents busy feeding them. Away each one flew. The moment the little birds heard their wings fluttering among the leaves, five yellow mouths flew open wide, so that nothing could be seen but five yellow mouths!

"Can anybody be happier?" said the father-bird to the mother-bird. "We will live in this tree always, for there is no sorrow here. It is a tree that always bears joy."

Soon the little birds were big enough to fly, and great was their parents' joy to see them leave the nest and sit crumpled up upon the branches. There was then a great time! The two old birds talking and chatting to make the young ones go alone! In a little time they had learned to use their wings, and they flew away and away, and found their own food, and built their own nests, and sang their own songs of joy.

The Robin Redbreast.
From *Mamma's Stories about Birds*
by Mary Elizabeth Southwell Dudley Leathley (1818-1899).

Then the old birds sat silent and looked at each other, until the mother-bird said, "Why don't you sing?" And he answered, "I can't sing — I can only think and think." "What are you thinking of?" "I am thinking how everything changes: the leaves are falling off from this tree, and soon there will be no roof over our heads; the flowers are all going; last night there was a frost; almost all the birds are flown away. Something calls me, and I feel as if I would like to fly far away."

"Let us fly away together!"

Then they rose silently, and, lifting themselves far up in the air, they looked to the north: far away they saw the snow coming. They looked to the south: there they saw flowers and green leaves! All day they flew; and all night they flew and flew, till they found a land where there was no winter — where flowers always blossom, and birds always sing.

HENRY WARD BEECHER.

Some of the prettiest stories you will hear were told by Mr. Henry Ward Beecher, who used to live in New York City. He was a great preacher and good story-teller. You will hear another of his pretty stories before many weeks. This one was taken from his book entitled "Norwood."

FOURTH WEEK OF SEPTEMBER.

WE have noticed the neatness of the birds; how they bathe in clean water, and what care they take not to get their pretty feathers soiled. The kitten washes her face, and steps very carefully not to get her little paws in a bit of mud. If you watch closely, you can see even the tiny flies brush their heads and cleanse their bright little faces.

Children ought surely to be as careful about clean faces and hands as kittens, puppies, and house-flies!

[Any of the stories of cleanliness given below may be used; and in some kindergartens they may all be told.]

"Tom the Water-baby" was written by Mr. Charles Kingsley for his own little boy. Mr. Kingsley lived in England, and was a great preacher. He also knew a great deal about the little animals that live in the sea, and has written some books for men and women that are full of beautiful thoughts.

[A picture of Canon Kingsley, and any little sketch the teacher may choose to give of his life, will perhaps help to form a taste for the best in literature. His song, "I once had a Sweet Little Doll, Dears," is a great favorite with children.]

Chimney Sweep.

From *The Century Illustrated Monthly Magazine*, Nov. 1901.

TOM THE WATER-BABY.

Once upon a time there was a little chimney-sweep, and his name was Tom. That is a short name, and you have heard it before, so you will not have much trouble in remembering it. He lived in a great town in the North country, where there were plenty of chimneys to sweep. He could not read nor write, and did not care to do either; and he never washed himself, for there was no water up the court where he lived. He had never been taught to say his prayers. Tom and his master, Mr. Grimes, set out one morning for Harthover Place, where they were to sweep the chimneys. Mr. Grimes rode the donkey in front, and Tom and the brushes walked behind.

Old Mrs. Earth was still fast asleep; and, like many pretty people, she looked still prettier asleep than awake. The great elm-trees in the gold-green meadows were fast asleep above, and the cows fast asleep beneath them; nay, the few clouds which were about were fast asleep likewise, and so tired that they had lain down on the earth to rest, in long white flakes and bars, among the stems of the elm-trees, and along the tops of the alders by the stream, waiting for the sun to bid them rise and go about their day's business in the clear blue overhead.

Tom never had been so far into the country before; and longed to get over a gate, and pick buttercups; but Mr. Grimes was a man of business, and would not have heard of that.

Soon they came up with a poor Irishwoman, trudging along with a bundle at her back. She had a gray shawl over her head, and a crimson madder petticoat. She had neither shoes nor stockings, and limped along as if she were tired and footsore; but she was a very tall, handsome woman, with bright gray eyes, and heavy black hair hanging about her cheeks. And she took Mr. Grimes's fancy so much, that when he came alongside he called out to her, —

"This is a hard road for a gradely foot like that. Will ye up, lass, and ride behind me?"

But, perhaps, she did not admire Mr. Grimes's look and voice; for she answered quietly,

"No, thank you; I'd sooner walk with your little lad here."

"You may please yourself," growled Mr. Grimes, and went on.

So she walked beside Tom, and asked him where he lived, and all about himself, till Tom thought he had never met such a pleasant-spoken woman.

And she asked him, at last, whether he said his prayers; and seemed sad when he told her that he knew no prayers to say.

Then he asked her where she lived; and she said far away by the sea that lay still in bright summer days, for the children to bathe and play in it; and Tom longed to go and see the sea and bathe in it.

At last they came to a spring, bubbling and gurgling, so clear that you could not tell where the water ended and the air began.

There Grimes stopped, got off his donkey, and clambered over the low road-wall, and knelt down, and began dipping his ugly head into the spring; and very dirty he made it.

Tom was picking the flowers as fast as he could. The Irishwoman helped him. But when he saw Grimes actually wash, he stopped, quite astonished; and when Grimes had finished, and began shaking his ears to dry them, he said,

"Why, master, I never saw you do that before."

"Nor will again, most likely. 'Twasn't for cleanliness I did it, but for coolness. I'd be ashamed to want washing every week or so, like any smutty collier-lad."

"I wish I might go and dip my head in," said poor little Tom. "It must be as good as putting it under the town-pump; and there is no beadle here to drive a chap away."

"Thou come along," said Grimes. "What dost want with washing thyself?"

Grimes was very sulky, because the woman preferred Tom's company to his; and he began beating him.

"Are you not ashamed of yourself, Thomas Grimes?" cried the Irishwoman, over the wall.

Grimes seemed quite cowed, and got on his donkey without another word.

"Stop!" said the Irishwoman. "I have one more word, *Those that wish to be clean, clean they will be; and those that wish to be foul, foul they will be.* REMEMBER."

How many chimneys Torn swept at Harthover Place I cannot say: but he swept so many that he got quite tired, and lost his way in them; and coming down, as he thought, the right chimney, he came down the wrong one, and found himself standing on the hearth-rug in a room the like of which he had never seen before.

The room was all dressed in white: white window-curtains, white bed-curtains, white chairs and white walls, with just a few lines of pink here and there.

The next thing he saw was a washing-stand, with ewers and basins, and soap and brushes, and towels; and a large bath full of

No, She Cannot Be Dirty.

By Jessie Willcox Smith, 1916.

clean water. And then, looking toward the bed, he held his breath with astonishment.

Under the snow-white coverlet, upon the snow-white pillow, lay the most beautiful little girl that Tom had ever seen. Her cheeks were almost as white as the pillow, and her hair was like threads of gold spread all about over the bed.

She never could have been dirty, thought Tom to himself. And then he thought, "And are all people like that when they are washed?" And he looked at his own wrist, and tried to rub the soot off, and wondered whether it ever would come off. "Certainly I should look much prettier, if I grew at all like her."

And looking round, he suddenly saw, standing close to him, a little, ugly, black, ragged figure, with bleared eyes and grinning white teeth. He turned on it angrily. What did such a little black ape want in that sweet young lady's room? And behold, it was himself reflected in a great mirror, the like of which Tom had never seen before.

And Tom, for the first time in his life, found out that he was dirty; and burst into tears with shame and anger; and turned to sneak up the chimney again and hide, and upset the fender, and threw the fire-irons down, with a great noise.

Under the window spread a tree, with great leaves, and sweet white flowers, and Tom went down the tree like a cat, and across the garden towards the woods.

The under-gardener, mowing, saw Tom, and threw down his scythe, and gave chase to poor Tom. The dairy-maid heard the noise, jumped up and gave chase to Tom. A groom ran out, and gave chase to Tom. Grimes upset the soot-sack in the new-gravelled yard, and spoilt it all utterly; but he ran out, and gave chase to Tom. The ploughman left his horses at the headland, and one jumped over the fence, and pulled the other into the ditch, plough and all; but he ran on and gave chase to Tom. Sir John looked out of his study-window (for he was an early old gentleman), and he ran out, and gave chase to Tom. The Irishwoman, too, was walking up to the house to beg; she must have got round by some by-way; but she threw away her bundle, and gave chase to Tom likewise.

Tom ran on and on, and when he stopped to look around, he said, "Why, what a big place the world is;" for he was far away from Harthover, having left the gardener, and the dairy-maid, and the groom, and Sir John, and Grimes, and the ploughman all behind him.

Through the wood he could see a clear stream glance, and far, far away the river widened to the shining sea, and this is the song Tom heard the river sing: —

> Clear and cool, clear and cool,
> By laughing shallow, and dreaming pool;
> Cool and clear, cool and clear,
> By shining shingle, and foaming wear;
> Under the crag where the ouzel sings,
> And the ivied wall where the church bell rings,
> Undefiled, for the undefiled;
> Play by me, bathe in me, mother and child.
>
> Strong and free, strong and free,
> The floodgates are open, away to the sea;

Free and strong, free and strong,

Cleansing my streams as I hurry along;

To the golden sands, and the leaping bar,

And the taintless tide that awaits me afar,

As I lose myself in the infinite main,

Like a soul that has sinned and is pardoned again.

Undefiled, for the undefiled;

Play by me, bathe in me, mother and child.

Then he fell asleep and dreamed that the little white lady called to him "Oh, you're so dirty; go and be washed;" and then he heard the Irishwoman say: *Those that wish to be clean, clean they will be.* And all of a sudden he found himself, between sleep and awake, in the middle of the meadow saying continually, "I must be clean, I must be clean." And he went to the bank of the brook and lay down on the grass and looked into the clear water, and dipped his hand in and found it so cool, cool, cool; and he said again, "I must be clean, I must be clean." And he put his poor, hot, sore feet into the water; and then his legs. "Ah," said Tom, "I must be quick and wash myself."

And all the while he never saw the Irishwoman: not behind him this time, but before.

For just before he came to the river-side, she had stepped down into the cool, clear water; and her shawl and her petticoat floated off her, and the green water-weeds floated round her sides, and the white water-lilies floated round her head, and the fairies of the stream came up from the bottom, and bore her away and down upon their arms; for she was the Queen of them all; and perhaps of more besides.

"Where have you been?" they asked her.

"I have been smoothing sick folk's pillows, and whispering sweet dreams into their ears; opening cottage casements, to let out the stifling air; coaxing little children away from gutters and foul pools; doing all I can to help those who will not help themselves: and little enough that is, and weary work for me. But I have brought you a new little brother, and watched him safe all the way here."

But Tom did not see nor hear this, for he had not been in the water two minutes before he fell fast asleep, into the quietest, sunniest, coziest sleep that he ever had in his life. The reason of his delightful sleep is very simple: the fairies had taken him.

Ah, now comes the most wonderful part of this wonderful story. Tom, when he woke, — for of course he woke; children always wake after they have slept exactly as long as is good for them, — found himself turned into a water-baby.

And now happened to Tom a most wonderful thing; he came upon a water-baby.

A real, live water-baby, sitting on the white sand, very busy about a little point of rock. And when it saw Tom, it looked up for a moment, and then cried, "Why, you are not one of us. You are a new baby! Oh, how delightful!"

And it ran to Tom, and Tom ran to it, and they hugged and kissed each other for ever so long, they did not know why.

At last Tom said, "Oh, where have you been all this while?"

"We have been here for days and days. There are hundreds of us about the rocks."

"Now," said the baby, "come and help me, or I shall not have finished before my brothers and sisters come, and it is time to go home."

"What shall I help you at?"

"At this poor, dear little rock; a great, clumsy boulder came rolling by in the last storm, and knocked all its head off, and rubbed off all its flowers. And now I must plant it again with sea-weeds, and I will make it the prettiest little rock-garden on all the shore."

So they worked away at the rock, and planted it and smoothed the sand down round it, and capital fun they had till the tide began to turn. And then Tom heard all the other babies coming, laughing and singing and shouting and romping; and the noise they made was just like the noise of the ripple.

And in they came, dozens and dozens of them, some bigger than Tom and some smaller, all in the neatest little white bathing-dresses; and when they found that he was a new baby, they hugged him and kissed him, and then put him in the middle and danced round him on the sand, and there was no one ever so happy as poor little Tom.

"Now then," they cried all at once, "we must come away home, we must come away home, or the tide will leave us dry. We have mended all the broken sea-weed, and put all the rock-pools in order, and planted all the shells again in the sand, and nobody will see where the storm swept in last week."

And this is the reason why the rock-pools are always so neat and clean; because the water-babies come in shore after every storm to sweep them out, and comb them down, and put them all to rights again.

Cat and Mice. Illustration by Ernest Griset, 1843-1907.

STORY OF A MOUSE.

A very neat little Mouse once lived in the same house with an ill-natured old Cat. When this little Mouse left his bed in the morning, he always washed and brushed himself with great care, taking particular pains with his long tail, which he kept very sleek and pretty.

One morning the untidy Cat had not been able to find her brush and comb, not having put them in their proper place the day before; and when the Mouse ran past her, she snapped his pretty tail quite off because she felt so cross. The little Mouse turned and said, "Please, Mrs. Cat, give me back my long tail!"

Mrs. Cat answered, "I will give you your long tail if you will bring me a saucer of milk; I always like milk better than tails."

The little Mouse had no milk in his pantry, but he took his tin pail and went to the Cow, saying, —

"Please, Mrs. Cow, give me some milk, and I will give Mrs. Cat some milk, and Mrs. Cat will give back my long tail."

The Cow said, "I will give you some milk, but I must first have some hay." The little Mouse then took his wheelbarrow, and going to the farmer, said, —

"Please, Mr. Farmer, give me some hay, and I will give Mrs. Cow some hay; Mrs. Cow will give me some milk, and I will give Mrs. Cat some milk, and Mrs. Cat will give back my long tail."

The farmer said, "I would be glad to give you some hay, but my barn door is locked; if you will go to the locksmith, and get me a key, I will unlock my barn, and give you all the hay you can carry on your little wheelbarrow."

Then the little Mouse took his pocket-book, and went to the locksmith, saying, "Please, Mr. Locksmith, give me a key, and I will give the farmer a key, and the farmer will give me some hay, and I will give Mrs. Cow some hay, and Mrs. Cow will give me some milk, and I will give Mrs. Cat some milk, and Mrs. Cat will then give me back my long tail."

The locksmith said, "I must have a file with which to make a key; if you will get me a file, I will make the key with great pleasure."

So the little Mouse took his satchel, and went to the blacksmith, and asked him, saying, —

"Please, Mr. Blacksmith, give me a file, and I will give Mr. Locksmith a file, and Mr. Locksmith will give me a key, and I will give the farmer a key, and the farmer will give me some hay, and I will give Mrs. Cow some hay, and Mrs. Cow will give me some milk, and I will give Mrs. Cat some milk, and Mrs. Cat will give me back my long tail."

The blacksmith answered, "I need some coal to build a fire before I can make a file. If you will go to the miner, and get me some coal, I will be glad to make a file for you."

So the Mouse took his little cart, and went down, down into the dark earth, until he saw a man, with a lantern on his hat, and when he spoke to the man, the man said, "Well done, little Mousie, how did you get so far without a light?"

Mousie answered that he was quite used to playing in the dark, and now he must work night and day to get his tail again; and then he said, —

"Please, Mr. Miner, give me some coal, and I will give the blacksmith some coal, the blacksmith will give me a file, I will give the locksmith a file, the locksmith will give me a key, I will give the farmer a key, and the farmer will give me some hay, and I will give Mrs. Cow some hay, and Mrs. Cow will give me some milk, and I will give Mrs. Cat some milk, and Mrs. Cat will give me back my long tail."

Then the miner filled the little cart with coal; and the Mouse trudged up to the blacksmith, who gave him the file, which he put in his little satchel, and then ran as fast as his feet would carry him to the locksmith, who gave him a key, which he put in his pocket-book, and carried to the farmer, who unlocked the barn door, and gave him all the hay he could pile upon his wheelbarrow. Mousie took the hay to Mrs. Cow, who filled his little tin pail with milk, which the Mouse carried to the cat, saying, "Now, Mrs. Cat, please give me back my long tail."

Mrs. Cat said, "So I will, my dear; but where have I put it?"

Then this untidy Cat called all the people in the house, saying, "Where could I have put that tail?" "Oh! now I think I know — I believe it is in the upper bureau drawer." But the tail was not in the upper bureau drawer, and the poor Mousie who had worked so hard was nearly ready to cry, and the milk was getting cold. Then Mrs. Cat said, "I must have put it in this closet," and she ran to the closet, pulling down dresses and boxes; but there was no tail there, and the little Mouse had to wink very hard not to let the tears fall, and the milk was getting blue, when Mrs. Cat shouted, "Of course I put it in the second drawer"; but she tumbled all the things out of the drawer and found no tail; then the little Mouse had to sing "Yankee Doodle" to keep from crying, and the milk was in danger of getting sour.

Mrs. Cat now clapped her paws, and said, "Why, I know where it is — I ought to have thought before — I put it here in this lower drawer, in this very box, wrapped up so neatly in pink tissue paper. Yes; hurrah! here it is! And the Mousie took his pretty, long tail, and ran home as fast as he could to get some glue to stick it on again; and Mrs. Cat ate her milk, thinking she would try hereafter to put things in their places.

[A whole series of clay-modelling may be derived from this story, the children — even the youngest — finding it easy to model a mouse, two small beads being used for eyes; the older ones making the saucer, the pail, the wheelbarrow, etc.]

Ermine.

THE ERMINE.

There is a beautiful little snow-white animal which is called an ermine, and there is a pretty legend about it, which you must know is not a true story, but is a most beautiful one, — so beautiful it ought to be true, Mr. Kingsley would say.

The ermine really has not a black hair on its exquisitely white body, and it steps very softly over the earth, that it may not soil even its snowy feet with the dust.

It is said there were once some naughty men, with dirty hands and faces, who thought it would be great fun to drive an ermine into the mud. They tried a long time without succeeding, for the ermine could run very fast, and creep into very small places.

At last these naughty men made a pen all around the ermine, with ditches full of muddy water on all sides but one, and on this side they built a hot fire; and then they laughed cruelly because the ermine must go in the mud or be driven into the fire.

When everything was ready, they shouted and ran after the little creature, which went bounding toward the muddy ditch; but it would not put a foot into such a vile place, and it ran to another side only to find that guarded with the muddy water. So it dashed from side to side; and when the cruel men pressed closer and shouted louder, reaching towards it with their foul hands, the glorious little ermine went flashing like a snow-flake straight toward the fiery wall that guarded the last side.

The men began to feel that there was not much fun after all in such sport as this, for they were not so wicked as to wish to burn the pretty ermine; but the ermine dreaded their unclean touch as much as she dreaded the mud, and while the men fell back in astonishment, the ermine leaped into the flame, — but in the flame appeared the dear Christ Child, who took the ermine in his arms and turned a glowing face upon the cruel men, saying:

"This is my ermine, white and pure as I made it. How dare you seek to harm it? I quench the fire that it may not be burned, for I am the Christ Child who cares for all things pure."

Then gazing pitifully upon the men, he whispered softly, "Go, make yourselves clean."

The ermine was carried to a beautiful garden, where it was never again afraid, and the men became gentlemen, who never teased another creature.

Adapted from Miss Phelps' poem entitled The Ermine.

STORIES FOR PRANG'S TRADE PICTURES.
No. 1. — The Farm-Yard.

Do you see the children in this picture? Their names are John and Mary, and they live on the farm, in a house which you cannot see, because the leaves are so thick on those trees behind the barn. They have come with their father to feed the pigeons and chickens; they have never been in a city but once, and they do not know the difference between an electric car and a horse car; but they could tell you what kind of trees the cows are under, and they could tell you that one of the cows is a Jersey; whose name is Dun, and that the beautiful cock is not of the same family as the hen with the little chickens. They might not know the difference between a street and a place, and they might think the postman was a police officer, but they could tell you the names of every kind of grass in the farm-yard, and of every flower that grows by the wayside, between their home and the schoolhouse, half a mile away; and they know the difference between thunder clouds and a mackerel sky.

That boy on the load of hay is their brother, and when he learns anything from the books, he dearly loves to teach it to the children from the earth or sky.

The Farm Yard.
Prang's Aids for Object Teaching, 1874.

Their father has promised them that he will harness the horses that you see in the barn, and will some day take them to visit their uncle who has a garden not far from a great city.

Look at that dog! his name is Eric, and he says, "Bow-wow!" That means, "May I go with you?" The old turkey spreads his tail like a large fan, and says, "Gobble, gobble, gobble!" Perhaps he means to say that he would like to see his cousins down at the garden. The hens say, "Kut-kut-ke-dak-kut!" The children answer, "Yes, we will take some of your eggs to our uncle," just as if the hens had asked them to do so.

The ducks say, "Quack, quack, quack!" Perhaps that means, "We would like a swim in the fountain basin at the garden." And the pigs say, "Oof, oof, oof!" No doubt they would like to root up some tulip bulbs and eat them, but corn is quite good enough for pigs, the children tell them.

That little calf says, "Baa, baa! Give me only half a pail of milk to-night and take the other half to the gardener." And the pigeons say, "Coo, coo, coo! We fly over the garden every day, but we love to come home every night and see the dear little children who feed us."

No. 2. — The Gardener.

The man who is on one knee in the garden is John's uncle, and the tall boy gathering fruit is John's cousin.

The others are hired to work in the garden and the greenhouse, which you see is covered with glass. One man is cutting the grass with a lawn-mower, and one is cleaning the gravel walk. They have had a letter that John and Mary are coming, and Uncle Toby is putting some flowers in pots which he is going to give them. Everything is clean and tidy about the garden.

The boy who is picking fruit is hurrying so he can have time to put John and Mary in the wheelbarrow and trundle them around the garden through the pretty paths. The spade and the rake, the watering-pot and the ladder, have each been used in the garden. Uncle Toby is a good workman, and he has saved so much money from the flowers he has sold, that he is having a new house built. Do you know what we call the men who build houses? You will be surprised to hear that the man who is boring a hole in the timber for the new house, is Uncle Toby's brother, and so is John's uncle.

The Gardener.
Prang's Aids for Object Teaching, 1874.

He is a very cheerful carpenter, and likes his work so well that he often tells the children he hopes they will be carpenters when they grow up. His name is Joseph — just the same name as that of a good carpenter who lived many hundred years ago in a far away country.

When he goes to his dinner he will be greatly surprised to find John and Mary there with their father and their Uncle Toby. The children will not have time to go to the new house to-day, but their Uncle Joseph promises to go after them himself some day and show them the tools that are used in building houses.

The Carpenter.
Prang's Aids for Object Teaching, 1874.

No. 3. — The Carpenter.

When the children went home from the gardener's, they had much to tell their brother about the plants and flowers, and the new house, about which they were to hear another day. Their brother taught them the names of the flowers their uncle had given them, and would you think it possible for one boy to know so much? He could tell them just what kind of roots the plant had, by looking only at the leaves!

The next week their Uncle Joseph came to take them to the new house, and he showed them boards, and shingles, and rafters, and clapboards, telling them the best kind of wood to use for floors, and how the lightest wood was used for lathes. The carpenters were glad to see children who looked about with so much interest and not once offered to touch a shining tool; and when John said he had a plant at home with leaves that had little teeth very much like those of the saw, the man who stands with his back toward us laid down his saw, put John on his shoulder, and called to his son who was sawing up there by the window, to take this little boy who used his eyes so well and give him some of the flower seeds he has in his pocket. John took the seeds, thanking both of the men for their kindness, and told them he was sure his brother at home could tell by looking at the seeds what the leaf would be; but the carpenter told him not to ask, but to plant the seeds, and wait patiently till they put forth leaves, and he would remember the longer for finding out for himself. John and Mary learned a great deal about nails and chisels, beetles and augurs, planes and saw-horses; and when they went home, their uncle gave them some clean bits of board and some sweet-smelling blocks of pine wood with which they made some little boxes, in which Mary keeps her doll's clothes.

NO. 4. —THE TINSMITH AND PRINTER.

When John and Mary went to their grandfather's on Thanksgiving day, they saw some uncles that work in the city. These uncles were their mother's brothers, just as Uncle Toby and Uncle Joseph are their father's brothers; and although the children had visited them once, it was when they were so small that they had quite forgotten about it, and these uncles said they thought it only fair that the children and their mother should spend a week in the city.

The Tinsmith.
Prang's Aids for Object Teaching, 1876.

Uncle John was a tinsmith, and the children went to his shop one day with their mother, finding him at work, as you see him in the picture. He is making an eaves-spout. Some days he works all day on tin pans, and other days on basins or boilers. He likes his work because he can make so many different things, and he says he always tells himself stories about everything he makes. The spout he is making he thinks will go in the country, — perhaps be put on Uncle Toby's new house, — and little children will hear the rain tinkling and splashing through it into the cistern; or if he makes a basin, he thinks about the child who may eat bread and milk from it, and he will imagine he sees the child in its home, with a pretty white kitten waiting for its share of milk from the bright basin.

He is a very good uncle, and can tell stories to children as fast as he can work, and that is so fast that people who are in a hurry for a bit of work always say, "We will take it to John King, for his work is always quickly and well done."

The Printer.
Prang's Aids for Object Teaching, 1876.

Uncle John left his shop one day to show the children the way to their Uncle Caxton's, who is a printer. Uncle Caxton is the handsome man turning the wheel with his foot to print the card he has in his hands.

When the children went to his office, he asked the man, who is putting little letters, called type, into their boxes, to please let the children find the letters of their names and bring them to him. They soon came with the tiny letters in their hands, and their Uncle Caxton showed them how to stick them in a little case; then he fastened the

The Progress of The Century - The Lightning Steam Press.
Published by Currier & Ives, 1876.

case in the machine, put some ink on the letters, and rolled a white card through, and there were the names

JOHN

AND

MARY

one on each card. The children were much pleased, and took the cards home with them, and showed them to the calf, who said, — ; to the turkey, who spread his tail wider than ever, and said, — ; to the cock, who flapped his wings, and said, —; to the hen, who ran from her nest, saying, — ; to the little yellow chickens, who picked at them with their little yellow bills, and said, — ; to the clucks, who curved their green and brown necks, and said, — ; to the pigeons, who shook their beautiful feathers, and said, — ; to the sleek horse, who said, — ; to the good-natured dog, who wagged his tail, and said, — ; to the pigs, who lifted all the bristles on their backs, and said, — ; and to somebody else, who said, "A card with John's name, and one with Mary's name too! Did the tinsmith make them for you?" The children laughed at this joke of their brother's, for he knew very well that tinsmiths are not the men who print cards. But the tinsmith had given the children something to take home with them. You can see a picture of one in the shop; but the one in the picture is larger than the ones the children had; they were made of tin, had wire handles, were about as large around as an orange, and were shaped like a cylinder, but were not solid; they would hold milk or seeds; yes, they were little tin pails painted red, and had JOHN in gilded letters on one, and MARY in gilded letters on the other.

How could the children use them?

They could carry water to the chickens.

They could carry seeds to the pigeons.

They could carry oats to the horses.

They could carry a drink of milk to their brother when he was at work in the hayfield.

They could gather them full of chestnuts.

They could fill them with snow in winter.

They filled them with popped corn for the carpenter when he came to visit them.

They filled them with roasted chestnuts for the gardener.

They packed them with ripe cherries for the printer.

And when spring came, and their father made maple sugar, they had two sweet little loaves made in the two pails, and when it was hard and smooth they slipped it out, packed it in a box, which John himself made from the little boards his uncle gave him when they were visiting the new house, and sent them to the city to their uncle, the tinsmith.

No. 5.—THE BAKER.

When Uncle John, the tinsmith, received this present from the children, he was much pleased, and wrote them this letter: —

"MY DEAR JOHN AND MARY:

"Your sweet spring gift came to me this morning, and brings a story with it. I thank you for the sugar, which looks too good to eat, and I hasten to tell you a story which I hope may come true.

"On a farm which you have seen there live two children whom I have not seen in a long time. These children have a cousin in the city who has just gone into business for himself; he buys tin spoons and cups and baking-pans and measures of me,— and I used to give him little pails like yours; but he is a man now and earns money for himself, and does not like to have his father give him any but Christmas and birthday presents. He says he has some little cousins in the country, — perhaps you know them,— and as the wheat from which he gets the flour for his bakery grows on a farm, and the eggs which he uses in making cakes come from a farm-yard, he would like very much to have his little cousins spend a week in the city and learn what they can about the way the city people must be helped by the country people.

"If my story may end by the little children coming here, I shall think it a very good story. Now ask your mother if you may come, and write me, 'Yes,' by return mail, so I may tell my son the baker to make some cakes for a birthday party, for I think little Mary's birthday comes next week, does it not?

"Your affectionate uncle,

"JOHN KING."

This letter made the children happy, for their mother said at once that they might go to visit their uncle and cousin. It took some time to get them ready, the winter ice and snow had spoiled their shoes, and they had to go to the village to buy some new ones and have the old ones mended. This took nearly a whole day; but the children enjoyed it, for the shoemaker told them about leather and lasts, pegs and waxed ends, soles and heels, until they almost wished they could stay a week in a shoemaker's shop. And they might have staid a week without hearing all that could be told about the whole process by which one child's shoe is made.

At last the day came for them to start, and the horses were harnessed to take them to the steam-car station, the little trunk was put in the wagon, and they kissed their father and mother good by, — for this time their brother was going with them, — and away they drove. But they had not gone far before one of the horses lost a shoe, and their brother said they must stop at the blacksmith's on the corner and have the shoe replaced, or the horse would be lame. At first the children thought they could not wait, but their brother told them there was plenty of time before the train would start for the city, so they stopped at the blacksmith's. You can see the smith in the picture; yes, that is the very horse that you saw in the farmyard picture.

The man with the hammer is making a horseshoe: you can see the shoe on the anvil. The boy at the bellows is keeping the fire bright and hot. Everybody is happy and busy. Even the children waiting outside are gathering some wayside flowers to take to the city.

The Baker.
Prang's Aids for Object Teaching, 1876.

When the shoe was firmly nailed on, the children started again, and met with no mishap during the remainder of their journey.

When they went to the bake-shop, they found their cousin wearing a white paper cap and a snowy white apron, — that is he, — just putting the cakes in the oven. While they are baking, he will tell the children about the little girl who brings the beans to be baked, and they will be glad so many beans grew in their father's field this year. They will learn that the cans of milk under the shelf came from a farm, that the barrels of flour came from the wheat that grew on a farm; in fact, that everything that we eat or wear can be followed back to the fruitful earth, and that is why we call it the good mother earth.

Now, I am sure you can make some stories for yourselves. Tell us about the woman behind the counter; tell us how long the children stayed in the city, and what they saw and heard; make a story about the lady buying shoes at the shoemaker's; about the roll of leather; tell what the shoemaker thinks or sings while he pegs away on that boot; who will wear the boot — perhaps that very boot will go across the seas, or climb the great mountains of our own country. Who will buy the shoes up there on the bracket? Who will buy the bread on the shelf in the bake-house? How will the money be earned with which to buy it? Who made the barrels that hold the flour? Where did the trees grow that furnished the wood for bread-boards and rolling-pins? Wake up, little children, and think about all you see in these wonderful pictures. Do you know who made the pictures and where the great Prang manufactory is? Some of you have sisters who work there.

Leaves.
From *Arbor Day Leaves* by N.H. Egleston, 1893.

FIRST WEEK OF OCTOBER.

HAVE you looked at the leaves that are turning red and gold and brown? By and by all the trees will go to sleep; the birds' nests in the branches will have no birds in them; the leaves will fall upon the earth and be covered with soft snow, and every branch of the trees will be bare and beautiful; then the children can see the slender shape of the twigs and their delicate colors. Some tree-trunks and branches are almost black, and others are so white that a great poet, Mr. Longfellow, called them the white ladies of the forest. Sometimes the young twigs are quite pink, and sometimes the body of a tree has beautiful patches of moss growing upon it. People used to love the

White-Oak.

From the Trousset Encyclopedia, 1886-1891.

trees so dearly that the poets believed a lovely woman lived in every tree, and when the wind rustled the leaves they thought the lady was singing.

Mr. Beecher wrote a story once which he called

THE ANXIOUS LEAF.

Once upon a time a little leaf was heard to sigh and cry, as leaves often do when a gentle wind is about. And the twig said, "What is the matter, little leaf?" And the leaf said, "The wind just told me that one day it would pull me off and throw me down to die on the ground!" The twig told it to the branch on which it grew, and the branch told it to the tree. And when the tree heard it, it rustled all over, and sent back word to the leaf, "Do not be afraid; hold on tightly, and you shall not go till you want to." And so the leaf stopped sighing, but went on nestling and singing. Every time the tree shook itself and stirred up all its leaves, the branches shook themselves, and the little twig shook itself, and the little leaf danced up and down merrily, as if nothing could ever pull it off. And so it grew all summer long till October. And when the bright days of autumn came, the little leaf saw all the leaves around becoming very beautiful. Some were yellow, and some scarlet, and some striped with both colors. Then it asked the tree what it meant. And the tree said, "All these leaves are getting ready to fly away, and they have put on these beautiful colors because of joy." Then the little leaf began to want to go, and grew very beautiful in thinking of it, and when it was very gay in color, it saw that the branches of the tree had no color in them, and so the leaf said, "O branches, why are you lead color and we golden?" "We must keep on our work clothes, for our life is not done; but your clothes are for holiday, because your tasks are over." Just then a little puff of wind came, and the leaf let go without thinking of it, and the wind took it up, and turned it over and over, and whirled it like a spark of fire in the air, and then it fell gently down under the fence among hundreds of other leaves, and began to dream — a dream so beautiful that perhaps it will last forever.

HENRY WARD BEECHER, in *Norwood*.

THE WALNUT–TREE THAT WANTED TO BEAR TULIPS.

Many years ago, when your grandmamma's grandmamma was a little girl, there stood a tall young Walnut-Tree in the backyard of a tulip-dealer.

Now the Walnut thought he had never seen anything so beautiful as the little Tulips that were set out in the yard to be kissed by the Sun, who each day paid a visit of an hour to the Walnut.

The wonder is that the Sun did not stay longer to watch the pretty shadow-pictures which the Walnut began to make on the grass as soon as the Sun said "good morning."

Another wonder is, that the great Walnut ever thought of looking down at the dear little Tulips, when he might have looked up at the greater Sun. But so he did, and you and I will never know the why of a great many things smaller even than that, until we go up higher, to be taught by the dear Friend who knows everything.

Tulip.
By Balthasar van der Ast, 1620s.

However, the Tulips were very lovely, I assure you, with their scarlet and golden cups.

One day a wonderful sister Tulip was brought out. What color was she, do you suppose?

"Crimson?"

"No."

"Purple?"

"No."

I am sure you will not be able to guess, so I will tell you.

She was black, and she was softer than velvet, and more glossy than satin.

When the Walnut saw this beautiful Tulip, every little leaf danced in the air for joy, and every little branch bent low. You've seen the trees bending to kiss the children and the flowers that way, I am sure.

The Walnut did something else, which I will tell you, if you will promise not to tell the Hickory or the Chestnut. He dropped a little leaf at the Tulip's feet, which was written all over with a wonderful language that nobody but trees and flowers, birds and bees, and perhaps Mr. Tennyson or Mr. Kingsley, could read.

The Tulip did not seem to care about the leaf or the letter written on it, and we cannot tell whether she sent an answer back to the Walnut or not: be that as it may, the Walnut was not quite so happy after he sent the letter, but he began growing better.

And do you not think it wiser in our best Friend to make us good instead of happy, sometimes?

The Walnut used to say after this happened, "I'll bear Tulips myself."

How would a Walnut-Tree look with Tulips among its leaves?

You think that could never, never happen? We shall see.

Walnut struck his roots deeper, and spread his branches broader and broader, until he was quite wonderful to look upon. Sometimes the Wind used to hear him singing something like this, which was set to the most beautiful, rustling little tune you ever heard: —

> "We'll bear Tulips yet;
> Leaves and I can ne'er forget;
> Roots, be not weary;
> Heart, be thou cheery;
> The blessing may tarry,
> But we'll bear Tulips yet, —
> Leaves, roots, and heart, do not forget."

A hundred years went by, but there were no Tulips among the leaves of the Walnut-Tree. A hundred years is a long time for trees to wait, is it not? We can afford to wait longer for some things than can the trees, for we never, never really and truly die. Now at the end of the hundred years this Walnut fell to singing another refrain which the years had been teaching him: —

> "I bear no Tulips yet;
> And though I ne'er forget,
> As thou wilt, Master, let it be,
> Tulips or only leaves for me,
> Still I will cheery be:

Do thou thy will with me;

Leaves, roots, and heart, I yield to thee."

This dear Walnut had been very brave and stout-hearted. He had left nothing undone which any Walnut-Tree could do, and he had grown very fine in fibre and perfect in form, so that one day a wood-carver said, "That perfect tree is just what I want for my work." The brave old Walnut was cut down and sawed and chipped; but he did not mind; for what do you suppose the wood-carver was making?

Black Tulips, to be sure!

You never saw any black Tulips?

Then I advise you to look sharply at every bit of wood-carving you can find; for those very Tulips are somewhere, feeling very happy that they can bloom all the year round, while some of the Tulips we know have to sleep half the year at least.

[Any hard-wood tree, more familiar to the children, may be substituted for the walnut; and if they are familiar with any particular leaf or flower in wood-carving, the story may be modified to suit the carving.]

Black walnut tree in winter.

THE WALNUT-TREE THAT BORE TULIPS *(continued)*.

The Tulips carved from the heart of the patient Walnut-Tree adorned the temple for which they were fashioned more years than the tree had struggled with the storms of its old life.

The carved petals grew darker with age, and the Walnut's heart of hearts became more peaceful with "self-devotion and with self-restraint." On Easter day the altar was adorned with living Tulips whose hearts were aflame with life and love; the cup of a splendid black Tulip was lifted to touch the dark wood of the carved altar, and the heart of the old Walnut throbbed with a divine discontent which was so softened by divine patience that it hardly knew it sang: —

"Father, I'm waiting yet,

Hoping thou'lt not forget.

Others I strive to bless,

Asking no happiness

But what thou wilt.

Carven and still I stand,

My life in thy dear hand."

Thus it poured out its melody while the people worshipped, and when a misplaced candle set fire to the altar draperies, and the great cathedral shriveled and crackled in the flames, the Walnut yielded its Tulips to the elements without fear, almost without hope, but with an infinite satisfaction in having given itself bravely and uncomplainingly to the Father's great plans, which must include a higher happiness for somebody than the heart of a Walnut could devise or perhaps even hold.

The ashes of the Walnut-Tree lay white and ghastly upon the charred earth; the dew gathered upon them, and the rain beat them deeper and deeper into the pitiless dust. At first they lay in the form of the Tulips, but the wind soon whirled the pale petal-shaped mass into pathetic shapelessness, and there lay the heart of the Walnut, forgotten of all but the unforgetting Father.

They yielded themselves now to winter's frost and summer's heat with no will but to suffer, and no hope but to bless unknown lives in His way, though only by enriching the earth for other blossoms.

A gardener passed that way, and like the woodman of old, selected that which best served his purpose, — the self-prepared earth. A Tulip bulb was buried in this fruitful soil, and by the beautiful chemistry of nature the Walnut-Tree found its carved, burned, and storm-beaten heart transformed into the living beauty of a magnificent black Tulip.

Is not this enough, — a hundred years of growth; a struggle with storms; a final fall beneath the woodman's axe; the sharp instruments of the wood–carver; the adorning of the temple; after which the flame and the frost; the loss of identity except to the Father; burial and final resurrection for one week of bloom in the color and form of a Tulip?

Nay, it is not enough, and the bright Tulip lifts its chalice, heart of Tulip answering to heart of child: —

"There is no death; there is only change. Live for others while you keep your own good purpose unchanged as the unchanging Father's love; forget selfish aims, yielding your life to wiser plans than any you can imagine; and, like the Walnut-Tree, you will find at length a joy too deep for any language but that of blooming in sweet and sacred silence."

Coal Anthracite.

HOW COAL IS MADE.

"What an amount of preserved sunshine there is in those little fragments!" said Cousin Ben, as we sat by the open grate.

"Is it preserved sunshine, Ben, that makes the coal burn?" asked Ralph. "Could sunshine get down into a deep coal mine?"

"Yes; the heat comes to us because the sunshine of a time long past was laid up for our use now. It is one of the best gifts our good Friend has given us. It keeps our houses warm, and gives us the light we burn. All kinds of machinery are worked by it, from the steam engines that take us to town, to the factories where all our goods are made."

"I don't see how it was done," added Ralph, whose second question had not been answered.

"Have you never been told that coal is made from plants? The heat of the coal is what plants first took in from the sun.

"I have been in coal mines where I could see shapes of ferns and other leaves. It has taken many whole forests to make a single mine.

"Peat is the beginning of a coal mine before it grows hard. In it you would see the stems of plants plainly."

"Is coke coal not quite finished?" asked Ralph.

"No. Coke is what remains of coal when the gas that we burn has been driven out of it.

"Tar oozes out of lumps of coal, making little black bubbles.

"Most of our beautiful dyes that we see in silks and woollens, and the flavors in our candies, come from coal tar also.

"Think of having heat, light, colors, and flavors stored up for our use deep down in the earth. Isn't it wonderful?"

From STICKNEY'S READER.

Sisters.

Lewis Wickes Hine, photographer, 1911, 1908.

SECOND WEEK OF OCTOBER

I HOPE you often think about the many things your mother does for you, and how busily your father works for you. Older brothers and sisters, too, are often very kind to the little ones. I once knew a girl in grammar school who went a long distance every day to take her little sister to the kindergarten. She never had time to play tag with the other girls, because she had to hurry or be late to her own school; and she was always gentle with the little sister, often carrying her when it snowed, and wrapping her own thin shawl about the child, who was usually much more warmly dressed than she was.

I knew a boy in the high school who brought his little sister to kindergarten every day, taking great care to hold the umbrella over her when it rained, and losing many a fine game with the boys of his own age because he chose to be kind to his tiny sister. What can the tiny sisters do to show the older ones that they love them and are grateful for their care?

The man who wrote the story of the Mouse and the Lion lived many hundred years ago. His name was Æsop, and there is a book of his stories which men, women, and children still delight in reading.

He was a slave at one time in his life, but his master was so charmed with his stories that he set him free.

A very rich king invited Æsop to live in his palace with him, so that he might listen to his wonderful stories every day. The great story-teller was so much loved and honored that the people of the city of Athens had a beautiful statue erected in his honor.

THE LION AND THE MOUSE.

A hungry Lion lay fast asleep in a thick wood.

And there were some little Mice who lived near by. They saw the great creature, and thought it would be fine sport to play Hide and Seek on his back.

So one little Mouse hid in his thick mane; another ran under his paw. One crept behind his tail. The smallest one of all ran over and over his back, to find those that were hiding.

The little Mice knew it was not quite safe, but they said it was all the more sport.

Suddenly, with a great gape and stretch, the Lion woke.

How the Mice ran! — all but the little one that was under his paw. It, poor thing, was held fast, and could not get away.

The Lion was hungry and a little cross. His first thought was to eat his poor little prisoner.

But the brave Mouse put up its tiny paws, and looked the Lion straight in the face.

"Do not eat me, O Lion!" she said. "Pray do not eat me! I'm such a little thing I should do you no good. And I've a mother and five brothers and sisters at home who would be so sad. If you will let me have my life now, I will do as much for you some day, indeed I will."

This made the Lion laugh. But he was not a bad Lion. He lifted his paw, and away ran the Mouse. Before her little brothers and sisters had time to tell what had happened to her, she was safe by her mother's side. How happy they all were, and how they praised the good Lion!

It was long afterward when a strange thing happened. One of the Mice — the very one that had been under the Lion's paw — was near the place where they had had their play. She heard the roar of a lion, and had a mind to run quickly away. The sound came again. "I know that roar. It is my old friend," she said. "I will go and see what is the matter."

There lay the Lion, roaring dreadfully. "What is the matter?" said the Mouse, in her little squealing voice; but the Lion did not hear.

So she went nearer, and spoke louder. She had to go close up to his ear to make him hear.

"What is the matter?" she said again.

"Don't you see," said the Lion, "how I am tied up with these ropes?"

"Oh," said the Mouse, "that is too bad."

She went and looked at the great rope that held the Lion fast. He had been bound with a great cord, by the hunters, who had gone for help to put the Lion in a cage. "Do not roar so loud, dear," she said, in a motherly voice; "I will see if I cannot set you free."

"What nonsense!" said the Lion, and he filled the air with his roaring.

The Lion and the Mouse.

From *The Æsop for Children with Pictures by Milo Winter.*

When he was still again, she said, "If you will lie still and not roar, I am sure I can save your life."

"How can you?" growled the Lion.

"What are my sharp little teeth good for, if I cannot gnaw your rope so that you can get away?" said the Mouse.

It took a long time. The Mouse was afraid all the time that the Lion would snap at her and eat her up. But he lay still and looked at her as she worked so hard at the rope.

"What makes you so kind?" he said at last.

"Do you remember," said the Mouse, "that you gave me my life once? When I was a young and giddy little child, you woke and found me under your paw, and you let me go free. I said I would do as much for you. I am doing it now, am I not?"

"You have saved my life," said the great Lion.

And there was another story to tell at the mouse home after that.

From ÆSOP'S FABLES.

[Miss Dugan, who wrote half of the stories about the Cow, lives in Boston, and first told these stories to the children of Cottage Place Kindergarten. She also wrote the words and music to several Christmas carols, especially for the little children of Cottage Place.]

MILK, BUTTER, AND CHEESE.

FIRST STORY IN SERIES OF OBJECT LESSONS ON THE COW.*

Little Alice was five years old, and had lived all her life in a city. She knew nothing of woods, and brooks, and fields full of clover and daisies, of bees, and butterflies, and birds, except through stories. Alice liked to hear these stories, and when she was snugly tucked in her little white bed, she would say, "Now, mamma, please tell how the cows showed you the way home that time you were lost," or, "Tell how you played with the little brook in the woods."

---

* Photographs showing ten consecutive images of a cow running by Eadweard Muybridge (1830-1904), published 1881.

A Little Girl and Cow.

From *A Child's Garden Of Verses* by Robert Louis Stevenson,

with Illustrations by Bessie Collins Pease, 1905.

Alice's father and mother loved their little girl very dearly, and when they found that she was growing pale and quiet, instead of being rosy and active as a healthy child ought to be, they began to think what would be the best thing to do for her. "She is drooping just as a flower would, if shut off from the warm sunshine and pure air, in a narrow street," said the mother.

"Then we must take our little flower to the country, where air and sunshine are plentiful," said the father, "and give it a chance to grow." Mr. Boyd was a busy man, and he had not left his work for a day since his little Alice was born; but he was a wise and careful father, and he did not wait long after deciding what was the right thing to do.

In less than a week Alice, with her father and mother, was speeding out of the city, on their way to a real country farm. As the piles of brick buildings were left behind, and the sky widened and lifted to the great boundless arch of blue, Alice raised her wondering eyes to her mother; but when they neared field and woodland, and she saw leaves glistening and dancing in the sunlight, water rippling over pebbly bottoms, white daisies nodding to each other by the roadside, her cheeks flushed with excitement, and she danced first on one little foot, then on the other, for very joy. You happy country children, to whom all these things are sweet and natural as the air you breathe, can you think what it was to a city child to see them all for the very first time? It was a long ride, and Alice grew tired. It was dark, and the stars were out, when they left the train, and Alice was fast asleep in her father's arms. When she opened her sleepy eyes, she found herself in a long, low room, where a table was set for supper, with the whitest of table-cloths and shining ware. Everything was cheery, and bright, and clean, and the room was sweet with the fragrance of red roses that filled a great jar in the open fireplace, and even climbed up outside and peeped in at the open window, as if they, too, wished to see and welcome the little visitor. Alice lifted her eyes in astonishment, and saw a kind, motherly face smiling down at her. She couldn't help smiling back, — everybody always smiled back at Aunt Lizzie, — and the two were friends at once.

Oh, how good that supper tasted to little Alice! Never had she eaten such yellow butter, such bread, such strawberries, red, and large, and juicy; and as for the thick, golden cream that Aunt Lizzie poured over her berries, our Alice had never seen anything like it in all her life. She whispered, "Mamma, do we eat custard on our berries?"

"Bless the dear child!" said Aunt Lizzie, "has she never seen cream before? Do you know what a cow is, little one?"

"I saw some in a picture once, and mamma told me about them. They give milk."

"The cow gives you a great many things besides milk, little daughter," said her father.

"How many?" she eagerly asked.

"Let me see your two hands," said Mr. Boyd.

Alice held them up. "Now spread out all your fingers and thumbs. There! I think you will find that the good cow gives you something for each little finger and thumb."

"Truly, papa? Will you tell me all about them?"

"You must try to find them out for yourself; but mamma, Aunt Lizzie, and I will help you. You can ask us all the questions you wish."

"You shall see the cow to-morrow morning," said Aunt Lizzie, "and learn where the milk comes from that you will drink for your breakfast."

Alice's first thought next morning, when the early golden sunbeams touched her eyes and opened them wide, was of Aunt Lizzie's promise. She was quickly dressed, and ran down stairs and out into the yard. Oh, how lovely and fresh was the morning!

Alice sat down on a long wooden bench that stood by a fence, separating the yard from a great field full of dewy grass. She peeped through the bars and wondered what made the grass so wet, and then she turned to look at Aunt Lizzie standing in the doorway under the climbing roses. Something very warm and sweet was breathed against her cheek from behind, and she gave a jump and looked round.

"It is one of the cows, our good Lightfoot," said Aunt Lizzie; "she is bidding you good morning."

Alice looked rather timidly at the great creature with shining red sides and big, crumpled horns; but Lightfoot's eyes were so large, and soft, and gentle, and she stood so quietly looking over the bars, that Alice soon put up her hand to pat her, and again she felt the cow's warm breath, sweet as the clover she had been eating.

"Here comes Luke to milk her," said Aunt Lizzie.

Luke had a bright tin pail in one hand, and a queer little wooden stool in the other. He swung himself over the fence, put the stool on the grass beside Lightfoot, and seating himself, put his pail under the cow. Alice looked wonderingly at the great, soft udder, as Luke took hold of the cow's teats, and then clapped her hands with delight when the white, foaming milk came streaming into the pail.

Imported Jersey Cow "Duchess."
From *The Jersey, Alderney, and Guernsey Cow*,
By Willis Pope Hazard, 1872.

"Oh, Aunt Lizzie, I've seen the real milk coming!" shouted Alice.

"You can count one on your little thumb now; one good thing we can thank the cow for giving us," said her father, coming out to enjoy his little girl's pleasure.

Aunt Lizzie brought a pretty china cup; Luke filled it with the warm, new milk for Alice to drink, and she said, "Thank you, dear Lightfoot."

When the pail was nearly full, and Luke was walking off with it, Aunt Lizzie said, "Come, little Alice, and see what becomes of the milk." Round the house they went to a low stone building. Entering, Alice found herself in a cool, airy room, where a little spring of water bubbled up right in the middle of the stone floor. The walls were lined with pans full of milk, and platters holding rolls of yellow butter.

There was something else, white and round, that looked very nice, Alice thought, but she did not know its name. She saw Luke pour the new milk into shining pans and set it away. There were two women here at work. One had a shell in her hand, and with it was taking something from the top of the milk. "Why, it is the cream!" said little Alice; "but why does she put it in this high tin roller?"

"That is a churn," said Aunt Lizzie, "and if you watch Molly, you will see what can be made out of milk."

Alice stayed and talked with Molly, even helping send the dasher up and down with her own hands, and was delighted to see the cream grow thicker and thicker, till the yellow butter began to appear. She held up her forefinger then, and said: "That counts one for the butter, doesn't it, Aunt Lizzie? I can hold up two fingers now."

"Come back to the house, and I will show you something for the tall middle finger," said Aunt Lizzie. Alice tripped along the path, Molly and Aunt Lizzie following with two great pails of milk. These were emptied into a tin boiler that stood over the kitchen fire. More milk was brought, and after it was heated, Aunt Lizzie put in a curious, brownish substance which she told Alice was rennet, and came from the stomach of a calf.

Alice was greatly interested, when after this the milk to grow thick and form curds. She watched Aunt Lizzie chop the curds and press them till all the thin liquid whey was squeezed out of them, and they were salted and pressed in a round, solid form like those in the dairy, each cheese being put into a large hoop of wood, until it became of

Cheese Press.
From *The Saturday Magazine*, Dec. 26th, 1835.

the right shape.

"See! this is a cheese, Alice"; and then kind Aunt Lizzie let Alice press and salt a tiny cheese with her own hands. How pleased and proud was the little girl when it was placed on the supper table, and mamma, papa, and even Aunt Lizzie each ate a small piece of Alice's own cheese.

"Does the cow give us anything else to eat'?" she asked.

"All in good time, little daughter," said her papa.

"You have learned quite enough for one day. Another time ring finger shall have a chance to stand up with the others."

CARO A. DUGAN.

Pure Jerseys — "Hopewell," "Clemy," and "La Belle Helene."
From *The Jersey, Alderney, and Guernsey Cow,*
By Willis Pope Hazard, 1872.

THIRD WEEK OF OCTOBER.

WE have made some very pretty beads, marbles, and bird's-nests from the clay, haven't we? Some of the smallest children have tried very hard to make pretty things with the clay, and our friends at home have been much pleased with the little presents we have made them. We like to do things for others, and we know others like to do things for us. Some children like to do hard things. I've seen very small children button their own boots and coats, and weave hard patterns in mats, much preferring to help themselves whenever they can. It is good for us to think about what others do for us. We should be grateful to the shoemaker who makes our shoes; the baker who makes our bread; the carpenter who builds our houses; and every-body who even speaks pleasantly to us.

There are some things which no man can do for us. No man can make the sun shine upon us, and no man can bring the rain upon the grass and flowers. No man can cause the stars to glow or the moon to shine at night.

LEATHER.

SECOND STORY IN SERIES OF OBJECT LESSONS ON THE COW.

When Alice was getting ready for bed one night she asked her father to tell her a story, and as she drank her cup of milk she thought of the good cow, and said, "Oh, papa! tell a story for my third finger; here is milk for my thumb, butter for my first finger, and cheese for my middle finger; my third finger wants something; I am sure the cow can give me something to count on this little ring finger!"

"Yes, Alice, I remember a story I read once," said her papa, "and I will tell it; but you must keep your mind busy with what I say; for I think I will make you guess a riddle this time. Take off your boots and put them on this cricket; get your slippers and sit here on my knee."

Alice hurried to do as her papa had bidden, and was soon sitting on his knee, earnestly listening to this old and oft-repeated story: "There was once a king who had not learned how to do many things; his people knew as little as he did about making houses, dishes, or clothes for themselves; they lived in tents and wore coarse clothes, not yet having learned to weave fine cloth. I think they made some garments from the bark of trees; they went with bare heads and bare feet all of the time.

"One day the king's horse fell dead under him, and there were no servants with him who were strong enough to carry him; so he was obliged to walk a long distance. The sharp stones cut his feet, and the briars pricked and tore them, until the king was in a great rage and said he would never again leave his tent until the earth should be carpeted for his feet.

"Then all his people began making coarse carpets, and at the end of a year they asked him to walk out and try the new carpet. He went out, and was greatly pleased; for the earth was so covered with the people's carpets that no sticks or stones could touch his feet; but when night came, he refused to go back to his tent, but bade them make a tent where they were, so he could pursue his journey next day. The people were greatly frightened, knowing he would soon come to the end of the carpet if he journeyed in this fashion. One of the servants went away by himself and spent the night in work; some of them went about crying and wringing their hands; while others made a few yards more of the carpet for the earth and hastened to spread it at the end of that already finished. Next day when the king came to the end of the carpet he was very angry and was going to have all the servants beaten, when the one who had worked all night came forward, and kneeling before the king, said, 'Sire, I have a carpet for the whole earth, though none but the king may walk upon it.' The king asked if it were like the paltry one whose limit he had reached in two days, and the servant replied, 'Nay, gracious king; thou canst

Shoemaker.

From *The Book of Trades, or Library of the Useful Arts, Part II,* 1806.

climb mountains, and thy feet be not bruised; thou canst wander in valleys, and thy feet never be torn by brambles; thou canst tread the burning desert, and thy feet remain unscorched.' 'Ah!' cried the king, 'bring me that priceless carpet, and half my kingdom shall be thine.'"

"Oh, papa!" said Alice, "did he really have a carpet like that?"

"There's my riddle, little girl; can you guess how he carried such a carpet as that in a sack?"

Alice, answered, "I must think hard," and closing her eyes with her hands, she said in a disappointed tone, "He must have been a magician"; but her papa told her he was no magician: then she thought again, but could not guess, and, opening her eyes, they fell upon her little boots on the cricket, and she clapped her hands, and shouted, "I know! I know! the servant had made the king some shoes." "You guessed rightly, my child, and now for your third finger; why shall we thank the cow for shoes?" Alice took the tiny boot in her hand while her father told her that the skin of the cow is used for the soles and heels of even cloth boots, and some coarse, heavy boots are made entirely of cow-hide. So Alice thanked the cow for her milk — there's one for her thumb; for butter — there's two for her first finger; for cheese — three for her middle finger; and for leather — which makes four, for the ring finger.

Thank you, thank you, thank you, thank you, good cow! I hope everybody will treat you kindly.

A Legend of The Great Dipper.
Stories For Kindergartens And Primary Schools
By Sara Eliza Wiltse, 1893.

A LEGEND OF THE GREAT DIPPER.

The faces of the stars shone so brightly one night that the earth children thought the Mamma Moon was telling a pretty story. And so she was, and this is the story: —

The Great Dipper, which you, my dear children, so love to form, has a deep meaning which you are not to forget as long as the stars shine. I will tell you the story as often as you ask it, and your asking makes me quite as happy as my telling can make you.

See the dear baby stars running to make a small dipper, like their older sisters! said the Lady Moon softly to the great Mars, who bent over her chair as she spoke.

In another world than ours, continued the Lady Moon, there was once a great trouble and sorrow. No, it was not in the earth world, my dear, she said to a tiny star who always asked questions; it was not in the heaven world either, but in another far-away world, where many children lived. For some good reason, which only the Father knows, the people and children, the animals and every living thing, were suffering great thirst; and no water, nor dew, nor drop of moisture could they find anywhere.

It was very horrible, and the people were very near death.

A little child of that world went out alone in the dry, dark night, carrying a small tin dipper, and prayed very earnestly for just that little cup of water; and when she lifted the cup, it was brimming with clear, cold water, which would not spill, though she ran rapidly, her hand trembling with her faintness; for she did not taste the water, having prayed for another's need. As she ran, she stumbled and fell, for she was very weak; and when feeling about, trying to rise, she touched a little dog that seemed to be dying of its thirst, and the good child poured a few drops of the precious water in the palm of her hand and let the dog lap it. He seemed as much refreshed as if he had drank from a river.

The child could not see what happened to her cup; but we saw, and sang for joy. The cup turned to silver, and grew larger, the water not having become less, but more, by her giving.

She hurried on to give the water to one who was quite unable to come to meet her, — none other than her own dear mamma, who took the water eagerly, as one in a deadly fever of thirst, but without putting it to her lips; for she heard just then a weak moan which came from the faithful servant who tried to raise her mistress' head, but found she had not the strength. The mother pressed the dipper into the hands of the maid, and bade her drink; feeling her own life so wasted that one little cup of water could not renew it. And neither maid-servant nor mistress noticed that the dipper changed from silver to gold, and grew larger than before. The good servant was about to give each member of the family one spoonful of the precious water, when a stranger entered, dressed in a costume unknown in that country, and speaking in a strange tongue, but showing the same signs of thirst and distress as themselves. The maid-servant said, "Sacred are the needs of the stranger in a strange land," and pressed the dipper to the parched lips of the fainting man.

Then the great wonder was wrought! and the golden dipper flashed forth incrusted with the most precious diamonds, containing a fountain of gushing water, which supplied the thirsting nation as freely and surely as it had quenched the thirst of the little dog.

And the Stranger stood before them a glorious, radiant Being; and as he faded from their sight, a silver trumpet tone was heard to proclaim: —

"Blessed is he that giveth a cup of water in My name."

Legend of the Great Dipper.
From *The Standard Third Reader*
By Martin Grove Brumbaugh, 1899.

And the possession of a dipper blazing with diamonds is, in that country, a sure badge of royalty; for no one can buy or receive one as a gift, nor can fathers bequeath them to children.

Each child is given a tin dipper at its birth, and only by purely unselfish acts can the diamond one be wrought.

Some of the foolish people have not yet learned its secret, and they go about trying to exchange their tin for silver, by doing kind things. Sometimes they accuse the Father of All very bitterly, because they grow old possessing only the tin dipper; for the secret of the exchange can no more be told than the beautiful, flashing, sparkling diamonds can be purchased. Sometimes there are great surprises, when people give up the hope of such a possession, and forget themselves; for then they often find the castaway tin bearing evidence in silver, gold, or even diamonds, that they have become royal; but by that time they have no vanity because of their fortune. Only modest, thankful, brave, happy feelings possess the owners of diamond dippers.

The Lady Moon now lifted a white finger toward the east, which was growing rosy, and the baby stars all knelt a moment, looking like white-robed nuns at prayers. Then the morning wind swept aside the great blue, silken curtain of the sky, and the Mamma Moon followed her children into Heaven, to do or play whatever the Father had planned for them while they were out shining for his earth children.

FOURTH WEEK OF OCTOBER.

[Provide a bit of broken plaster for examination.]

LET us find all the things in this room that were made for us by others.

Tables made by the cabinet-maker, from wood which the trees furnish.

Chairs, flower-pots, vases, curtains, etc., etc.

[The teacher, of course, leaves the finding of most articles to the children, and as each is found, a little sketch of its manufacture is given.

If the story of the Cow is to be told, the observations will not be given up until the plaster on the walls is noticed.]

HAIR AND BONES.

THIRD STORY IN SERIES OF OBJECT LESSONS ON THE COW.

It was sunset, and Alice sat in the doorway under the roses, watching for Luke, who had gone to the pasture after Lightfoot and the other cows. Aunt Lizzie had a good many cows, — old Brindle and Pet and Jessie and White Lily and Brown Bess and Short-horns and Bell, — but Alice liked Lightfoot best of all, and every night watched for her coming, and stood by

Luke's milking-stool with her little cup to get a drink of new milk. This night Alice watched and waited in vain, for Luke did not come. The rosy sunset glow faded out of the sky; it grew darker, and here and there a star peeped out, but still Luke did not come.

"Alice, it is bedtime now," called her mother, and with a sigh of disappointment the little girl climbed the stairs to her room, and began to prepare for bed. While her mother was brushing out her long, soft hair, Alice heard a familiar voice, and flew to the window. There stood Luke, telling Aunt Lizzie that the bars of the great pasture were down, and the cows all gone. He had had a long tramp, but could not find them. "I will mount Tita at sunrise tomorrow and have another hunt," said Luke.

"Oh, may I go with you?" cried Alice; "can't two ride on Tita?"

Luke looked up, smiling to see the little white figure at the window, its bright hair blowing in the night breeze, and answered, "Oh, yes, Tita wouldn't mind carrying us both on her strong back; I'll take you if your mother is willing."

"Wouldn't she be a trouble to you?" asked Mrs. Boyd.

"Oh, no!" said Luke, smiling again. He and Alice were great friends.

"Oh, my dear Lightfoot!" said the child, as she nestled down in her little bed. "Mamma, do you think Lightfoot is lonesome way off there in the dark?"

"No, little daughter; you forget that Brindle and Jessie and Short-horns and the others are all with her, and I don't think she minds the darkness, while she has plenty of soft grass to lie upon. Only think how pleased she will be to see her little mistress coming for her in the

Cattle. By Paul Potter (1625-1654).
From *The Theory and Practice of Perspective* by G. A. Storey, 1910.

morning." So Alice went to sleep with happy thoughts, after all. Very early next morning she rode out of the yard, seated before Luke on Tita's broad back. At first, when the horse's great shoulders began to move under her, Alice was a little afraid, and clung fast to Luke, feeling almost as if she were on a moving mountain; but she soon became used to the motion and felt safe and happy.

The eastern sky was full of golden light that grew and deepened until the great sun came in sight, and then how the dewy fields glistened and shone! Alice laughed with delight when she saw the silvery spider webs shining like little fairy tents in the wet grass, — "Sign of a fine day," Luke told her, — and the dear white daisies nodding good morning to the sun, and when they rode through woods where low-hanging branches sent showers of bright drops in their faces.

On they went through woodland and along the river, and at last far off across the river meadows they heard the faint tinkle of a bell.

"That is old Brindle's bell!" said Luke.

Tita pricked up her ears and trotted merrily on, and in a few moments they saw the horns of old Lightfoot herself. How glad Alice felt then; she could hardly wait to be lifted down from Tita. She threw her arms about Lightfoot's neck and hugged and kissed her for joy. What do you suppose Luke did? He took a tin cup from his pocket, saying, "You must be hungry, little Alice, after such a long ride," and in a moment he had it filled with Lightfoot's fresh milk. It tasted good to Alice, I assure you. She began, saying, "Thank you, Lightfoot, for milk, thank you for butter, thank you for cheese, thank you for leather, thank you again for milk."

"We are near the Gray's new house," said Luke, looking off through the trees; "come with me, and we will find how the cow helps us make houses."

"Does she really?" said Alice; "how can she?"

"Ah, that I will let you find out for yourself."

A few steps brought them to the new house. Several men were at work on the house.

"What are they doing?" said Alice; "that man is all sprinkled with white, — is he painting?"

"Not painting, but plastering," said Luke, "making the walls warm and tight with plaster, so no cold air can creep in next winter to chill the people who will live here."

Alice watched the spreading on of the wet plaster with great interest.

Little Girl and Cow.
From *Child Life in Prose,* 1875.

"Now see if you can find out how the cow helps make that plaster," said Luke.

Alice looked at it, and said doubtfully, "It is white like milk, but I shouldn't think milk would make good plaster."

"It is the lime that is white," said Luke; "step nearer and look very carefully."

"Why, it is full of funny little hairs, like cow's hairs," said Alice. "Oh, I know now; the good cow gives her hair to help make plaster," and up went one of her hands, with all the little fingers outspread, while she said, "Now, little baby finger, you may stand up with the rest, and thank the cow for hair to make plaster. Why do they put it in the plaster, Luke?"

"It holds it together better, and so makes a closer, warmer covering for the walls. Now if you come into the garden, perhaps we will find something that will make Mr. Thumbkin on the other hand stand up."

"Does the cow help make gardens as well as houses? What a good cow!" said Alice.

They found the gardener busy sprinkling the earth about young plants and vegetables with a kind of white powder.

"Did that come from the cow? What is it?" asked Alice.

"That is pretty hard for you to guess," said Luke.

"It doesn't look like this," taking a piece of solid white bone from his pocket, "but it really is made of the bones of the cow, burned and crushed to powder. It makes the earth rich, and so helps the plants to grow."

"Oh, my dear Lightfoot!" said Alice, when at last, mounting Tita, they began to drive the cows homeward, "how many things you are good for!" When they rode into Aunt Lizzie's yard, Alice held up two thumbs and four little fingers, calling out, "Oh, mamma, papa, Aunt Lizzie, — Luke has found me two new things that the cow gives us!" And as Luke lifted her off Tita's back, and she ran toward the house, so eager for breakfast, she looked back with a bright, friendly smile to say, "Thank you, Luke."

CARO A. DUGAN.

GRANDMA KAOLINE.

[Illustrate with a little old woman made of clay.]

I have somebody under my handkerchief to introduce to you. It is a very little, very old lady. I will go around and introduce all the quiet, polite children to her. "This is Grandma Kaoline, Johnny Jones."

[Grandma Kaoline can be made to bow by bending the finger upon which she sits.]

You will see that Grandma Kaoline is made of clay. I am going to tell you a strange and wonderful story about Grandma Kaoline.

The clay of which she is made was found down in the ground, in what people call a clay bed, or clay bank; sometimes it is called a clay mine. Grandma Kaoline is so very, very old, that while we talk about the clay, we will let her take a nap under my handkerchief — perhaps she will like that as well as some longer naps she has had in her other bed, underground.

Thousands of years ago, when the earth was very young — yes, millions of years ago, before little children came to live upon this beautiful earth, even before the earth had grown so beautiful, — there was no clay here with which to make pretty things.

If Grandma Kaoline could take you by the hand, and lead you back to that time, the world would look so strange to you that you would cry to come back to kindergarten. Grandma Kaoline could show you nothing but great rocks and oceans, with a few rivers of water. There were no birds, nor trees, nor flowers anywhere on the whole earth.

The Careful Gardener had not made them yet, but he knew he should send some little children to live here some day, and there were many things to be made for them, one of which was this clay. Great rocks were thrown up into the air by earthquakes; they were tossed into the rivers by winds; they were pushed and knocked together until they became smooth as glass ; then they were thrown into the air, as if a giant were playing ball with them, and their smooth sides broken until rough again. They were rolled down mountains, and washed in rivers, until they were ground to powder finer than flour.

This fine powder, ground from the rocks, was carried by the water into low places in the earth, and then it was laid to rest in cool, dark beds while something else was done by the Gardener, who took care of everything.

I cannot tell you all that was done for us before we came; but you shall hear of more wonderful things than this at another time; now we are only to talk about the powdered stones which lay in cool, dark, damp beds thousands of years, becoming clay at last instead of stone.

[Show a bit of granite.]

Do you think we could make this hard stone into soft clay?

Was it not kind of the Gardener to do for us what we could not do for ourselves?

FIFTH WEEK OF OCTOBER.

ARE we not happy children, since we can do so much for each other and for our mammas? Even the birds and flowers seem happier for our happiness.

Did anybody help you to dress this morning? Who buttoned your boots? Who brushed your hair? What did you do to help? Even the baby can help, by taking its bath without crying; I have seen little kindergarten children help very much by keeping quiet while having their hair brushed, and no one but mamma knows how much it helps for a little child to know just where it hung its hat and coat the last time it was worn.

[If the story of the Cow is to be told, the children may be brought into a state of wonder as to how the Cow could have helped them in getting ready for kindergarten.]

GRANDMA KAOLINE'S STORY.

You have heard a story about Grandma Kaoline, and now Grandma Kaoline may tell you a story about herself. We will play that Grandma Kaoline can talk, and you may listen to her.

I think these little children will learn to listen to the stories that the flowers and rocks, the grass and shells, have to tell.

"Once I lay in a bed which was larger than your crib, larger than your mother's bed, larger than this house; yes, larger than the whole city of Boston. My bed was down under the water, and I wondered what would ever be done with it. I wondered a great many years, and all the time I was wondering the bed was growing larger, until one day it was pushed up out of the earth, and lay in the sweet sunshine — to air, I supposed.

"It was lying there so soft, and cool, and smooth, when some strange-looking people came along. They were not riding in carriages; for they had not yet learned to make carriages. They were not riding on horses; for they had not yet learned to tame the horses, which were wilder than any untamed horse you ever saw. They were all walking. Their feet were bare; for they had not yet learned to make shoes for themselves. They wore but few clothes and what they did wear were made of the skins of animals for they had not yet learned to make cloth.

"They were thirsty, but they had no dishes from which to drink; for they had not yet learned to make dishes. So they dipped their hands in the pools, and drank from the little cup which we can all make in the palms of our hands.

"A very pretty woman with a very pretty baby made a cup for the baby from a large leaf. While she was getting the leaf she left the baby standing on the cool bed of clay; and when she came back to take him up, there were the prints of his two pretty feet, with each little toe as perfect as could be. The woman looked at the little cups made by the pretty baby feet; then she kissed the dimpled feet, tossed the baby over her shoulder, and went with the other people, who

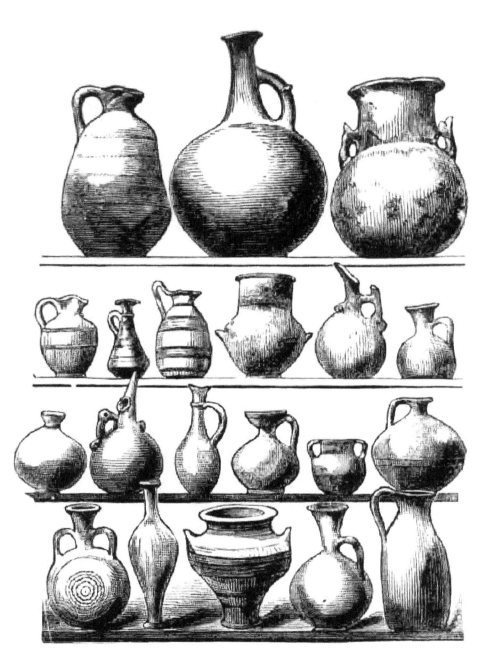

Phenician Vases.
From *Pottery and Porcelain of All Times and Nations*
by William Cowper Prime, 1878.

wandered around the country, not knowing how to do much of anything, but learning a little every day.

"After a long time these same people came back to the same place where the baby had stood in the clay bed, and what do you suppose the baby's mother saw? The two little cups made by baby feet had become quite firm and hard in the sunshine; and baby's father and mother both shouted, 'Look! look! Why can we not make dishes from this stuff?' The people ran like children, filled their hands with the soft clay, and made deep dishes, like vases, in which they could keep their seeds and grain; for they soon learned that water would make their new dishes crumble in pieces. After a long, long time somebody threw an old vase into the fire — the fires, you must know, were built upon the ground; for the people had not yet learned to make stoves, nor had they learned to make matches. It was therefore so hard to kindle a fire, when it went out, that they took great pains to keep one burning as long as they stayed in a place; and it was in one of these fires which burned many days that the old vase was thrown. You will see that the vase must have been well baked before the people went away to learn something else in their wanderings; but not knowing that a baked vase was any better than an unbaked one, they left it in the ashes. After a very long time they came again to this place, having learned to take better care of their babies, and to make better things for their own dinners. Somebody picked up the vase from the ashes, and found that it was very hard and smooth. They poured some water in it, and the water did not make it crumble; then they knew they could make dishes by baking the clay in a very hot fire, and they danced and shouted for joy that dishes could be made to hold milk and water. They built great fires and made more dishes than they could use; they amused themselves by making pictures on the unbaked dishes, with sharp sticks. These pictures would remain, of course. Sometimes we find one of these old dishes now. After many hundred years they learned to make china cups and saucers. They learned many other useful things; so that now, we, who are their great-great-great-great-great-great-grandchildren, live in good houses, have good clothes and good food, and are still learning how to use the things which the Careful Gardener has placed here for us."

[An impression strongly resembling a baby's foot can be made in the clay by doubling the hand and pressing the inside of the fist into the clay, the toes being added by indenting with the fingers. Showing these cups to the children increases their interest in the subject; and firing some of their best work, which can be done at trifling expense, will give them a living interest in, and knowledge of, pottery. A visit to a museum, where some ancient pottery may be seen, is also of great value to the eager learners.]

HORN.

FOURTH STORY IN SERIES OF OBJECT LESSONS ON THE COW.

 One day Alice came into the house bringing a bit of broken comb to her mother and asked how it happened to be such a light color, while her comb was black. He mother asked her if she did not think it might be an old black comb faded; but Alice felt sure it could not be, for she had seen old black combs that were not faded, though they had lain for weeks

Combs.

From *The Great Industries of the United States*, 1874.

in the sun and rain. Then her mother laughed, and said, "You have found something now for the pointing finger of your left hand; and if you can name the six things for which you have learned to thank the cow, we will go out to the pasture to see if you can find what the cow gives us that can be used in making combs."

Alice held up her thumb and fingers and counted very rapidly: —

"Mother Thumb, thank the cow for milk; that is one.

"Father Pointing Finger, thank the cow for butter; that is two.

"Brother Middle Finger, thank the cow for cheese; that is three.

"Sister Ring Finger, thank the cow for leather; that is four.

"Little Baby Finger, thank the cow for hair for plaster; that is five.

FIFTH WEEK OF OCTOBER.

"Mrs. Thumbkin, thank the cow for bones to make the plants grow; that is six."

"You remember well, Alice; come now with me and learn what part of the cow is made into combs."

Alice tied on her sun hat, and putting her hand in that of her mother she went out to the field of clover, where Lightfoot was standing under a tree, chewing her cud. Alice had never noticed Lightfoot's chewing before, except when she was nibbling the clover, and she went close to her head, and said, "Oh, Lightfoot! mamma says chewing gum is not a nice habit!" I do not think Lightfoot minded Alice's reproof, but she swallowed what she was chewing and began to smell at Alice's pocket, which pleased Alice greatly, for she had something in that pocket for the cow, but she had not expected the cow to find it so soon.

"What do you think Alice took to the cow in her pocket?"

"Clover?"

"No; there was all the clover in the pasture that the cow needed."

"Sugar?"

"No; the cow did not care for sugar, but it was something white and fine like sugar."

"Salt?"

"Yes; it was salt." Alice had learned that cows are very fond of salt; and when she took a handful from her pocket she laughed to feel the cow's rough tongue as she licked the salt from her hand.

Lightfoot was a gentle cow, and Alice thought her big brown eyes were beautiful. When the salt was all gone, and Lightfoot gave a last

"... she laughed to feel the cow's rough tongue."
From *Golden Moments* by Anonymous.

kiss to the little hand, Alice threw her arms about the good cow, and said, "You dear old bossy cow, where do you keep combs? I'd like to learn. I've seen you comb your own glossy hair with your tongue, but your tongue does not look like this comb," and she took the bit of comb from her pocket and held it up before the cow, who did not act as if she had ever before seen a comb, or cared whether she should ever see another; in fact, she gave an odd little sound in her throat as if she were going to say something about the salt, and up popped her cud, which she began chewing again as if Alice had never rebuked her about it.

This surprised Alice very much, and she asked he mother where Lightfoot kept her food? Mrs. Boyd then told her that cows and some other animals chewed their food several times before it was taken deep into their stomachs; that they swallowed it into a place called the first stomach, where they let it lie until they wanted it, when it could be raised for another chewing.

"That would be a nice arrangement for little girls who like strawberries and ice-cream so much," said Alice; but her mother reminded her that she must find that part of the cow which looked most like the comb about which they had come to learn.

"I see! I know!" said Alice; "her horns look almost like this comb!"

"Yes," said her mother; "when the life goes out of the cow's body, her horns are sent to a place where they are made into combs; so you see the cow serves us as long as she lives, and then she leaves us her body to use. I think some lazy people would be put to shame if they honestly compared themselves with Lightfoot. I hope my little girl will never become one of those women who serve no purpose in life." Alice could now count seven fingers, and she pointed the seventh at the cow and shook it playfully, saying, "Thank you, cow, for horn for combs."

From The Tortoise and the Hare.

From *The Æsop for Children with Pictures by Milo Winter*.

THE HARE AND THE TORTOISE.

A Hare one day made himself merry over the slow pace of the Tortoise, and vainly boasted of his own great speed in running.

The Tortoise took the laugh in good part. "Let us try a race," she said; "I will run with you five miles, and the fox shall be the judge."

The Hare agreed, and away they started together.

The Tortoise never stopped for a moment, but jogged along with a slow, steady pace, straight to the end of the course.

But the Hare, full of sport, first outran the Tortoise, then fell behind; having come half-way to the goal, he began to nibble at the grass, and to play with other Hares at hide and seek. After a while, the day being warm, and being tired with play, he lay down for a nap, saying, "If she should go by, I could easily enough catch up with her and pass her."

When the Hare awoke, the Tortoise was not in sight; and running as fast as he could he found her at her goal, comfortably dozing, while the Fox stood waiting to tell the Hare he had lost the race.

From ÆSOP'S FABLES.

[This story can be illustrated with clay animals, — after which the children can each model a Hare and a Tortoise. The most unskillful can represent the long–eared Hare, and the Tortoise is very easily modeled.]

FIRST WEEK OF NOVEMBER.

WHEN we break a toy or a chair, or anything made of wood, can we mend it with needle and thread as we mend our dresses when we tear them? Is it a neat way to mend a broken chair with nails and hammer? Look at the tables and chairs, and see if they are fastened together with nails.

[A chair may be made with the blocks of the third gift, and a table with those of the fourth gift, or with any bits of blocks that have been contributed.

Some of the older children might put on the glue (not mucilage), and the miniature piece of furniture be set away to dry.

This exercise and lesson will afford both amusement and instruction, whether used as a preparation for the fifth story of the Cow or not.]

GLUE.

FIFTH STORY IN SERIES OF OBJECT LESSONS ON THE CAW.

 Alice had a doll that she thought was the best and dearest doll in the world. Her mother gave it to her when she was quite a little girl, and she had always taken as good care of it as if it were a real, live baby. The doll had a china head, its hair was yellow, its eyes brown, and its cheeks very

pink. It had two white dresses and a great many sashes, made out of bits of ribbon given to Alice from time to time.

It had a tiny straw hat trimmed with brown ribbon and a bit of brown feather, to wear when it went out to walk, and a pretty white nightdress to put on at night. The good Luke had made a dainty little bedstead for Alice, and Aunt Lizzie had given her a mattress, and sheets, and pillows, and a blanket and quilt; so every night when Alice went to bed, the dolly went too, and slept in its own wee bed beside its little mother.

One morning, after breakfast, Alice said, "Now, Gretchen," — that was the doll's name, — "we have a great deal to do this morning. We must help Aunt Lizzie make butter, and we must help Luke pick the strawberries for dinner. Only you mustn't eat many, Gretchen, while you are picking, — only two, three, five you may eat."

Gretchen looked very smiling, as if it mattered little how few strawberries she had, as long as she was with Alice. Round the house they went, following the little foot-path to the dairy, where it was so cool and pleasant. Alice liked to go there often to see the sweet, yellow butter made from Lightfoot's milk. I think it helped Aunt Lizzie more to see her happy little face, and hear her talk to Gretchen, than even when Alice's little hands took hold of the churn dasher and made it go up and down, to "rest" Aunt Lizzie. After the butter came, and Molly was busy working and salting it, Alice and Gretchen went to the garden and helped Luke hunt for strawberries under the green leaves. Alice worked very busily, and I don't believe she ate more than the two, three, five berries she had promised Gretchen, she was so eager to fill her tin pail.

Broken Doll.
From *Sing–Song* by Christina Georgina Rossetti
Illustrated by Arthur Hughes, 1893.

How glad she felt when it was heaped to the brim with rich, red berries, and she could take it to the house to show mother and Aunt Lizzie! She walked up to the door, carrying the pail carefully in one hand, and holding Gretchen with the other. Her mother came to meet her, asking, "Did my little girl pick all those strawberries herself?" Before Alice could answer, she hit her foot against the great, flat door-stone, and over she went, the strawberries rolling in every direction in the grass, and what was far worse, Gretchen falling on the big stone with such force that the pretty china head was knocked completely off her body.

Alice cried when she picked herself up and saw poor little headless Gretchen. "Never mind, dear; we will ask the good cow to help us, and we shall have Gretchen all right again before long." Alice was so astonished that she stopped crying, to ask, "Why, mamma, do you mean that the cow can really put my Gretchen's head on again?"

"Yes, Alice; I think Gretchen's fall will give your tall middle finger a chance to stand up with the others."

With her mother's help Alice picked up the scattered berries, none the worse for their roll on the soft grass, and then the two went into the house, and Mrs. Boyd asked Aunt Lizzie where she kept her glue.

"Glue, mamma?" said Alice; "that is what papa used to mend chairs with; does the cow give us that?"

"Yes," said her mother; "it is made from the cow's hoofs. After the cow dies, her hoofs are washed and cleansed and made into this brown sticky glue."

While she was talking, Alice's mother was spreading the glue with a brush on the rough edges of poor Gretchen's neck. Then she took the head and pressed it carefully and firmly down into place again. Alice danced about, exclaiming, "My dear Gretchen! may I have her now, mamma?"

"No, dear; we must put her away till tomorrow, when the glue will be dry and hard. Now let me see how many fingers you can hold up."

Up went one little hand, and Alice said, "Thumbkin, thank the cow for milk; Pointer, for butter; Middle Man, for cheese; Ring Man, for leather; Little Man, for hair. Now the other hand. Thumbkin, thank the cow for bones; Pointer, for horn; and Middle Man, for glue. Only two more fingers! I wonder what they will tell me! Oh, mamma! I love Lightfoot better and better every day. I will make something for her now while I am waiting for Gretchen."

What do you think it was? It was made of white daisies, and was something Lightfoot could wear. Yes, it was a chain for her neck, — a long, beautiful daisy chain.

Alice worked hard, and had it all ready when Lightfoot came to be milked; and as Luke lifted her up so she could throw the chain over the cow's horns, she said as fast as her little tongue could say it, "Thank you, thank you, thank you, thank you, thank you, thank you, thank you, thank you, dear good Lightfoot!"

Can you tell me why she thanked the good cow eight times?

CARO A. DUGAN.

Home to Thanksgiving.
Published by Currier & Ives, 1867.

SECOND WEEK OF NOVEMBER.

BY and by we shall have a holiday. Some of us will go away to see our grandmothers or our cousins, and some of us will stay at home and perhaps have friends come to visit us. But whatever we do, we must remember why we have no schools or kindergartens on that Thursday, and why all the stores are closed so that everybody can rest or play for one day.

It is so that everybody may have time to say, "I thank you" to our Best Friend.

The First Thanksgiving, 1621.
By J.L.G. Ferris.

[The familiar Thanksgiving song, "Over the river and through the woods," may be dramatized, greatly to the delight of the children, especially if the teacher will wear a cap and glasses to personate the grandmother. "How the Sparrows were fed on Thanksgiving Day," by Miss Laliah B. Pingree, may be told to the children. Miss Pingree lives in Boston, and was superintendent of the kindergartens for many years, having herself taught in a kindergarten at Jamaica Plain before being connected with all the kindergartens of the city. This story was written for the children of Boston, at the urgent request of many of the teachers, and it admirably supplied a long-felt need for a good Thanksgiving story. Its results were widespread and lasting. No doubt the little contributions for the birds are still made in many kindergartens.]

THANKSGIVING STORY.

It was nearly time for Thanksgiving Day.

The rosy apples and golden pumpkins were ripe, and the farmer was bringing them into the markets. One day when two little children named John and Mary were going to school, they saw the turkeys and chickens and pumpkins in the window of a market, and exclaimed: —

"Oh, Thanksgiving Day!"

"Oh, Thanksgiving Day!"

And after school was over they ran home to their mother and asked her when Thanksgiving Day would be.

She told them in about two weeks; then they began to talk about what they wanted for dinner, and asked their mamma a great many questions. She told them she hoped they would have turkey and even the pumpkin pie they wanted so much, but Thanksgiving Day was not given us that we might have a good dinner, but that God had been a great many days and weeks preparing for Thanksgiving. He had sent the sunshine and the rain and caused the grains and fruits and vegetables to grow; and Thanksgiving Day was for glad and happy thoughts of God, as well as for good things to eat.

Not long after, when John and Mary were playing, Johnnie said to Mary: —

"I wish I could do something to tell God how glad I am about Thanksgiving Day." And Mary said, "I wish so too."

Just then some little birds came flying down to the ground near them, and Mary said, "Oh, I know!" Then she told Johnnie; but they agreed to keep it a secret until the day came.

Now, what do you think they did? I will tell you. They saved their *pennies* and bought some corn, and early Thanksgiving Day, before they had their dinner, they went out into the street near their home and scattered corn in a great many places. What for? For the birds.

While they were doing it, Johnnie said, "I know, Mary, why you thought of the birds; because they do not have any mammas or papas after they are grown up to get a dinner for them on Thanksgiving Day"; and Mary said, "Yes."

By and by the birdies came and found such a feast! and perhaps they knew something about Thanksgiving Day, for they sung and chirped happily all day.

LALIAH B. PINGREE.

[A brief historical sketch of Thanksgiving Day may be told the children who are old enough to comprehend it.]

STEAK AND TALLOW.

SIXTH STORY IN SERIES OF OBJECT LESSONS ON THE COW.

Alice had been promised a real picnic in the woods, and the day after her doll was so beautifully mended with the glue, the family began making ready for the "woods party," as Alice chose to call it.

You may be sure Lightfoot gave her share for the dinner: her milk helped to make the buns; her butter helped to make the cake; her cheese was packed beside the doughnuts

High Door Curtain Rockaway.
From *Appleton's New Practical Cyclopedia.*

which Aunt Lizzie made, and in the morning when the family rock-a-way* was driven to the door, Alice was so happy that she could hardly wait for the others to get their places. She took the little seat which seemed made for her and shouted to her papa to be sure to get the jug of cream; to her mamma, not to forget the milk, to the pony, not to overturn the rock-a-way while she ran back to the house to get her doll, who would cry her blue eyes blind if she were left at home: then she ran up and down stairs, to the cellar and garret, just because she was too happy to stand or sit still while the grown folks were packing the luncheon. Finally they were quite ready to start, and the pony trotted briskly off, not seeming to mind Alice's "whoas" or "go alongs" any more than he did the doll's hold of the ends of the reins.

Alice looked surprised when her father stopped at a meat market in the little village and took her in while he bought a few pounds of tender steak; but he said, "That's for your lesson out in the woods to-

---

* Editor's note: Rock a-way, A light, four-wheeled, two-seated pleasure-carriage. From *A Dictionary of The English Language* by Noah Webster, 1892.

day." Alice was glad to have the promise of a lesson from her father, for his lessons were always easy to learn, she thought.

They drove over a straight road that made Alice think of a wide sash ribbon, it looked so smooth and long; then they turned into a shaded road that wound along the bank of a pretty little river, and Alice got out of the rock-a-way a dozen times to pick a handful of flowers. There were wild purple asters, bright golden-rod, and brilliant red flowers upon slender stems that Alice had never seen before: her father told her it was cardinal flower, and he was much pleased that she remembered the name.

When they left the river bank, they climbed a rocky hill, where the pony was taken from the harness and given some oats, which they had not forgotten to bring; for Alice's father was kind to horses as well as to children.

They found a bright little spring of clear, cold water bubbling up between two great rocks; they found a flat rock which served for a table, and while Mrs. Boyd and Aunt Lizzie were setting the table, Mr. Boyd gathered some pine needles and dry branches, with which he kindled a fire beside a great rock: he then cut a slender green bush, and trimming off its leaves, made one end of it quite sharp, upon which he held the meat in the fire. Alice grew hungry as she smelled the sweet odor of the roasting meat, and asked her papa to hurry a little with the lesson, or she should get too hungry to listen. Mr. Boyd cut off a bit of the meat and gave it to her, saying perhaps she would remember without much talking that she was to thank the cow for the steak, as it was part of a cow, her life having gone out and left her flesh for our use.

Alice counted her fingers again; "Thank you, cow, for milk, butter, cheese, leather, hair, bones, horn, glue, and steak."

When the meat was all roasted, they took it to the table, and agreed that such roast beef as that made the picnic dinner the best they ever ate. Alice made them laugh by saying it was the best picnic feast she ever saw. She had never been to a picnic before, and she could not see why she should not call it the best.

When they started home, Mr. Boyd said, "Let's drive around the other way home, so we may see new sights." And Alice was very happy to go a new way; but after they had driven several hours, and things looked newer and stranger, Aunt Lizzie said they would do better to find the home road, she thought, and Mr. Boyd said, "Just what I've been trying to do more than an hour!"

And they all confessed that they knew nothing about the road they ought to take to get home.

Alice woke her doll to ask if she knew the way home; but she did not know, and having been asleep, had a good excuse for being lost. She asked the pony if he knew the way home, and he neighed as if he wished he were there, but could not tell them where to go. It grew late, and Mr. Boyd said they would stop at the next farmhouse and stay all night if it were too far for them to drive home.

Alice was pleased with the prospect of spending the night in a new place, and hoped there would be a little girl who had a doll in the next farmhouse.

The next house was rather small, but there was a little girl and a doll, and a bed to spare for the strangers.

Head of Cow.
Published by Detroit Publishing Co., between 1890 and 1901.

Alice thought it great fun for her papa to sleep on a sofa in the sitting-room; for there was no bed for him. The little girl who lived in the farmhouse was named Ruth, and she offered her crib to Alice and her doll.

When it grew dark, Alice was very much surprised to find that there was neither gas nor lamps in the house, but she was too polite to ask questions about it. Ruth's mamma, however, lighted several candles, so that the room was very pleasant, and after she had lighted Ruth's white-haired grandmother to her room and kissed her good night she came back to say that grandma was so much afraid of lamp explosions that they had never used one, though the candles gave rather a dim light. Alice's mamma said a house with love in it like that could never be dimly lighted.

Alice thought she might ask Ruth how candles were made, and Ruth was very happy to tell her how they used the fatty part of cow's flesh. Alice forgot where she was and jumped up, clapping her hands and shouting, "That ten! that's ten!"

"Ten what?" asked Ruth.

"Why, ten things for which to thank the cow," answered Alice; "but please go on and tell me all about it."

Ruth brought in some tin candle-moulds and a ball of cotton called wicking, and showed Alice how the wicking should be threaded into the moulds, and the melted beef's tallow or fat poured in and then cooled, after which the candles could be drawn out of the long tin horns, as Alice called them.

Alice then told Ruth about the ten things the cow gives us, — milk, butter, cheese, leather, hair, bones, horn, glue, steak, and tallow.

The girls then played a game called "blow out the candle." Ruth shut her eyes and walked three steps backward from the candle, turned around three times and took three steps forward, and then tried three times to blow the candle out; but when she opened her eyes, she found she had been blowing at the door-knob. Alice tried it, and found she walked toward her mother, and had been puffing at her back hair instead of the candle, as she supposed.

The girls amused themselves in this way until bed-time; and the next morning when Alice started for home, — in the right road this time, — Ruth's mamma promised them that Ruth should come to make Alice and Lightfoot a visit before many weeks.

THIRD WEEK OF NOVEMBER.

DO you remember about the first week of kindergarten, how warm it was, — so warm that you came without wraps? Now what do you wear?

The birds have gone to the warm country; we have fires in furnaces, grates, and stoves. Apples and pears are ripe and have been gathered; the farmer has his corn and wheat in the barns, and is making the sheds warmer for his sheep and cows. For what do you think we are getting ready?

Some animals go to sleep when winter comes, and remain sleeping during the cold weather.

Bears, woodchucks, snakes, and toads sleep many weeks at a time; some of them in holes in the ground, and some of them in hollow trees.

This is a good time for us to think about what we can do for others. There are some people who do not think much about themselves, but are always trying to make somebody else happy; and some people have even spent their lives in trying to make horses, dogs, and cattle comfortable, and preventing others from hurting them. One man, who lived in New York, was so distressed on seeing the cattle crowded into cars without enough to eat or drink, that he determined to make them more comfortable; and now when cattle are shipped from one state to another, they have more room and plenty of air, food, and water. This same kind-hearted man could not sleep nights because he saw horses made to draw loads that were too heavy for them; and he talked about it to everybody he saw, and wrote about it in the newspapers; until others felt as he did; and now there is a society in nearly every city, which prevents unkindness to the animals. This good man's name was Henry Bergh, and every little boy and girl can help to make the world better and happier by being kind to stray kittens and dogs, and persuading other boys and girls to be fair with them.

STORY OF THREE BEARS.

Once upon a time there were Three Bears. They lived together in a house of their own in a wood.

One of them was a Little Small Wee Bear; and one was a Middle-sized Bear; and the other was a Great Huge Bear.

They had each a pot for their porridge: a little pot for the Little Small Wee Bear; and a middle-sized pot for the Middle Bear; and a great pot for the Great Huge Bear.

And they had each a chair to sit in: a little chair for the Little Small Wee Bear; a middle-sized chair for the Middle Bear; and a great chair for the Great Huge Bear.

And they had each a bed to sleep in: a little bed for the Little Small Wee Bear; a middle-sized bed for the Middle Bear; and a great bed for the Great Huge Bear.

"... and poured it into their porridge-pots."
From *The Golden Goose Book* with drawings by L. Leslie Brooke, 1905.

One day they had made the porridge for their breakfast, and poured it into their porridge-pots. Then they walked out into the wood while the porridge was cooling. They did not wish to burn their mouths by beginning too soon to eat it.

In that same far-off country there lived a little girl. She was called Silver Hair, because her light curly hair shone so brightly.

She was a sad romp; and so restless, she could not be kept quiet, but ran out and away, and often without leave.

One day she went into the wood to gather wild flowers, and into the fields to chase butterflies. She ran here and there and everywhere, till at last she found herself in a lonely wood.

There she saw the snug little house where the Three Bears lived when they were at home.

First she looked in at the window, and then she peeped into the keyhole, and seeing no one in the house, she lifted the latch.

The door was not locked; for the Bears were good Bears who did no one harm, and did not think any one would harm them.

So Silver Hair went in. And well pleased she was when she saw the porridge on the table.

She tasted the porridge of the Great Huge Bear, and found it too hot for her.

Then she tasted the porridge of the Middle Bear, and found it too cold for her.

And then she went to the porridge of the Little Small Wee Bear, and found it neither too hot nor too cold, but just right; and she liked it so well that she ate it all up.

Then little Silver Hair sat down in the chair of the Great Huge Bear, and that was too hard for her.

She sat down in the chair of the Middle Bear, and that was too soft for her.

And then she sat down in the chair of the Little Small Wee Bear, and that was neither too hard nor too soft, but just right.

But she sat in it so hard that the bottom fell out, and she fell through almost to the floor.

Then Silver Hair went up stairs to the chamber where the Bears slept.

And first she lay down upon the bed of the Great Huge Bear, but that was too high at the head.

And next she lay down upon the bed of the Middle Bear, and that was too high at the foot.

And then she lay down upon the bed of the Little Small Wee Bear, and that was neither too high at the head nor at the foot, but just right. So she lay down upon it and fell fast asleep.

While little Silver Hair lay fast asleep, the Three Bears came home from their walk.

They thought their porridge would be cool enough by this time, and they went to breakfast.

Now little Silver Hair had left the spoon of the Great Huge Bear standing in his porridge.

"SOMEBODY HAS BEEN AT MY PORRIDGE!" said he, in his great, rough, gruff voice.

And the Middle Bear looked at his pot of porridge, and said: —

"SOMEBODY HAS BEEN AT MY PORRIDGE!" in his middle voice.

And the Little Bear looked at his porridge, and said, in a little, soft, wee voice: —

"Somebody has been at my porridge, and has eaten it all Up!"

And so the Three Bears began to look about to find the thief.

"Somebody Has Been At My Porridge!"

Now little Silver Hair had not put the hard cushion straight when she rose from the chair of the Great Huge Bear.

"SOMEBODY HAS BEEN SITTING IN MY CHAIR!" said the Great Huge Bear, in his great, rough, gruff voice.

And little Silver Hair had pressed down the cushion the Middle Bear when she sat upon it.

"SOMEBODY HAS BEEN SITTING IN MY CHAIR!" said the Middle Bear, in his middle voice.

And you know very well what Silver Hair had done to the third chair.

"Somebody has been sitting in my chair, and has sat the bottom out!" said the Little Bear, in his little, soft, wee voice.

Then the Three Bears thought they would search further; so they went up stairs to look into their chambers.

Now Little Silver Hair had pulled the pillow of the Great Huge Bear out of its place.

"SOMEBODY HAS BEEN LYING ON MY BED!" growled the Great Huge Bear, in his great, rough, gruff voice.

And little Silver Hair had pulled the pillow of the Middle Bear out of its place.

"SOMEBODY HAS BEEN LYING ON MY BED!" said the Middle Bear, in his middle voice.

And when the Little Small Wee Bear came to look at his bed, the pillow was in its right place, but upon the pillow was the head of little Silver Hair, which was not in its right place, for she had no business there.

"Somebody has been lying on my bed— and here she is!" piped the Little Small Wee Bear, in his little, soft wee voice.

Little Silver Hair had heard in her sleep the great, rough, gruff voice of the Great Huge Bear; but she was so fast asleep that it was like the roaring of the wind, and she did not wake.

And the middle voice of the Middle Bear was as if she heard some one speaking in her dream. But when she heard the little, small, wee voice of the Little Small Wee Bear, it was so sharp and so shrill that it woke her at once.

Up she jumped; and when she saw the Three Bears at one side, she tumbled out at the other, and ran to the window.

Now the window was open; for good, tidy Bears they were, and always opened their bedroom windows when they got up in the morning.

Out Silver Hair jumped, and away she ran to her mamma, and told the story of the Three Bears; and the Bears invited in their neighbors to tell them the story of Silver Hair.

THE BEAR THAT HUGGED THE TEA-KETTLE.

A bear once came out of the woods late in autumn, to have one more walk before he should go to sleep for the winter.

A little farmhouse stood near the woods, and the boiling tea-kettle had been set out of doors on a little table by the woodshed.

The bear saw the steam puffing from the spout of the kettle, and perhaps had never seen such a sight before; for he hurried up to the table, and standing on his hind legs, put his nose into the hot steam to smell it. Of course his nose was burned, and he was angry with the tea-kettle, and jumping on the table he seized it in his hairy paws; but he dropped it very quickly and spilled some of the hot water on his feet. The little children who were looking out of the window at him were very glad to see him run away as fast as he could, and their mamma assured them the bear would not be likely to visit their house again that winter.

ANONYMOUS.

Fourth Week of November.

IF the sheep did not give us wool for mittens, hoods, cloaks, and dresses, I am afraid we would be uncomfortable some of these days. And if the shoemaker did not make our shoes, what should we do? Do you remember what birds stay with us during the winter? What can we do for them?

The men who build our houses should do the best kind of work, should they not? Suppose they were to leave cracks in the walls, as some children are apt to do when building with blocks? We must be careful to do neat work even while we are little children, and then when we are grown we will find it easy to do good work. We want no holes left in our new shoes, and we want our houses to stand very firm with walls and roofs strong, for the wintry snow and wind must not come inside. Everybody who does any kind of work ought to do it the best he can, not thinking about how easily or quickly it can be hurried away, but doing every part of it well. There is a beautiful church in Europe that is said to be just as perfect in every corner from basement to bell-towers as it is about the altar. The statues in all the little dark niches were carved by great sculptors, and the painting in every corner was done as if it were to be seen every day by the crowds who gather in the nave and transepts. Isn't that a beautiful and honest way to work?

I suppose it would take a whole lifetime to learn about all the people who have done beautiful things, and we have time in kindergarten to study only a few of them.

FLORENCE NIGHTINGALE.

There was once a rich and beautiful woman in England, who could not content herself to do nothing but ride in a carriage, wear fine clothes, and visit people who lived in castles. When she sat at her father's table with all the good things to eat and all the beautiful silver and glass and china before her, she would think of the poor sick people who had not even an orange to quench the thirst of fever. And when the news came to her father's house of the dreadful suffering of the English soldiers away off in Crimea, she told her people she must go there and help to take care of them. She had been a good nurse even when a tiny little girl, doing just what the doctor told her to do when anybody in the house was ill; and everybody loved to have her come into the room even when suffering with a dreadful headache, for she would step softly, and give the sufferer a drink of cool water, or turn a pillow, not making a bit of noise.

She went to the hospitals and took such good care of the soldiers that those who got well and went home wanted to make her a present of a large sum of money: but she told them she should not take money for herself, — that would not make her happy, — but they might give it to the city of London for a training school for nurses, so that there would be enough to take care of all the wounded soldiers next time they should be needed. The more this noble woman

Florence Nightingale.
Photo by Perry Pictures, 1910.

thought about others, the more people loved her, and the Queen sent her a beautiful jewel with her love and thanks for her goodness to the English soldiers; and the soldiers! think how they must have loved her! They wanted to have a statue of her raised in London, and they would give a penny apiece for the purpose, thinking she would not object to such a little gift; but she would not have the money used that way, telling them it would please her more if they would give it to the hospitals. But the world will not forget Florence Nightingale though there is no statue of her in London.

PEEP STAR! STAR PEEP!

One night the Stars said to the Moon, "Please may we stay out late tonight? We want to play hide-and-seek."

"You may stay as late as you please," said the Moon, "if you take good care of the baby Stars, and lead them gently so that none of them will fall."

So each Star took a baby Star by the hand, and led it out into the sky-garden, where the game was to be played.

That was a fine night for a child to look up into the blue sky; for the Stars were all out, — large Stars and small Stars, Stars that could run fast as a boy ten years old, and Stars that had to lie on little cloud-beds to watch the game, because they were too small to run without falling.

When the Stars play hide-and-seek, they do not cover their eyes with a bandage; for they can shut them so closely that even the Moon cannot be seen.

The oldest sister Star began the game by closing her eyes and counting ten, while the others held up their fingers for her to count, which, of course, no Star could do with her eyes shut.

When they were sure she could not see them, they kept their lips closed for fear a laugh would break out to tell where they were; and they ran on tiptoe until the sister Star spread out her arms and almost caught a dozen of them. Then they ran pell-mell under one of the little white cloud-cribs, and a child who was looking at them said: —

"I fink the Stars are playing peep-boo with me, mamma."

One of the Stars heard the little girl; for the Stars are very glad to play with children, and are much pleased when children make pictures of them, and ask questions about them; and the Moon is always willing the Stars should be friendly with children, though it often happens that a careless Star leans so far over the sky-garden wall, to look at some baby of earth, that he falls down, down, to the ground. It does not hurt Stars to fall as it does children, and the Moon is not lonely when one of her Stars comes down here; for she can see and hear them where-ever they are, and she knows better than your mamma does that one Father takes care of all children, so that to him none of them are ever lost; but the Star that falls to the earth does not shine any more, as it does when it is up in its own garden.

When you are older, you will learn about these meteors, and what relation they hold to Stars.

When the little child said she thought the Stars were playing "peep–boo" with her, the sister Star said, "Come; a child wants to play with us." And those beautiful Stars took hold of hands, and ran down a wide path in such a hurry, their white dresses and silver sashes fluttering about them, that to the little child looking at them they seemed like a snowy ribbon unrolled across the sky, and she cried out, "Oh, mamma! I see a pretty white sash — and mamma, mamma, it has little silver stars all broidered on it; do you think it is for some lady Star to wear to a party?"

A Visitor in the Morning Sky.
Elizabeth Shippen Green Elliott, artist, 1910.

Then the Stars laughed with glee, till the Moon held up her finger for them to listen to what a little boy, half-way across the world, was saying. He was talking to his papa; and when he saw all the Stars crowding down that bright path, he said: —

"Papa, I think those Stars are having a fine coasting-party."

The little boy's papa and the little girl's mamma said: —

"I am glad that the Sky Father is the Earth Father, too, and that the little Stars are just as well cared for as our children and ourselves."

When the Stars saw the Sun coming to put them to bed, the Moon and all her family knelt down, just where they were, some in the garden-path, and some on their cloud-beds, and told the Sky Father how glad they were that he could take good care of Stars as well as of the dear little children in the under-world. And they went to sleep up there just as the children and birds were waking here.

The Song of the Angels.

Engraved by Samuel Sartain from an original painting by Thomas Moran, 1872.

FIRST WEEK OF DECEMBER.

WE had a holiday last month: you remember we took time to say "thank you" to our best Friend. This month we shall have another holiday; it will be Christmas, the birthday of the Christ Child.

[The New Testament story of the shepherds watching their sheep, and the journey of the wise men, is perhaps the best Christmas story that can be told. The drawings illustrating this are among the most original that I ever saw children make.]

Christmas Eve—Getting Ready for Santa Claus.
Wood engraving, published 1876.

SECOND WEEK OF DECEMBER.

WE have to work very busily this month to make presents.

We love to do hard things, even if we are little children.

Out in the woods there are trees that are green all winter. We call them evergreens. There is one waiting out there to be brought to us and filled with our gifts for our friends.

[The blessedness of giving was never, perhaps, better demonstrated than in the kindergartens where the thoughts were turned upon making gifts instead of receiving them. At Cottage Place it was the custom for many years to fill the trees with the children's gifts to their parents and older brothers and sisters, no mention being made of any expected gifts in return. Every Christmas it was a fresh revelation to the teachers of the inherent generosity of child-nature; for notwithstanding the costly presents supplied the children every year after the distribution of their gifts to their parents, the next year found them engrossed with thoughts of giving, any reference to receiving being quite exceptional.]

There are many kinds of stories, — stories that are true and stories that are untrue. Some stories have been made by just one person, and others have been made by a great many people. Sometimes a story is told first in Germany; and when it is told in this country, a little change is made in it, and then it goes over to France, and is told in the French language with just another little change, until it has been in many countries and told in so many languages that it does not sound much like the first German story. Some stories have been growing hundreds of years — a true story in the beginning, but a little added or changed until we are unable to tell just what was true in the time of it; but there is so much that is so good and beautiful in these stories as we have them that we still love to hear them. Sometimes people tell a dream, and some one listening goes away and tells it as a true story, and so something untrue comes to be believed. There are some lovely stories that have been growing ever since the Christ Child came to earth, and some people have believed them and made pictures of parts of them. One is the story of

SAINT ELIZABETH AND THE SICK CHILD.

Once when Saint Elizabeth was ministering to her poor at Eisenach, she found a sick child cast out from among the others because he was so loathsome in his misery that no one would touch him or even go nigh to him; but Elizabeth, moved with pity, took him in her arms, carried him up the steep ascent to the castle, and while her attendants fled at the sight of the poor child, she laid him in her own bed. Her husband was absent, but shortly afterward his horn was heard to sound at the gate. Then his mother ran out to meet him, saying, "My son, come hither! see with whom thy wife Elizabeth shares her bed!" and she led him up to the chamber, telling him about the sick child. He rushed to the bed and snatched away the coverlid; but behold! instead of the loathsome child, there lay a radiant infant with the features of the Christ Child of Bethlehem; and while they stood amazed, the infant smiled and vanished from their sight.

Saltmarsh Sharp-Tailed Sparrow.
From the *Trousset Encyclopedia*, Paris 1886-1891.

THIRD WEEK OF DECEMBER.

A JEWISH LEGEND.

I LIKE that old, kind legend
Not found in Holy Writ,
And wish that John or Matthew
Had made Bible out of it.

But though it is no gospel,
There is no law to hold
The heart from growing better,
That hears the story told: —

How the little Jewish children,
Upon a summer day,
Went down across the meadows
With the Christ Child to play.

And in the gold-green valley,
Where low the reed-grass lay,
They made them mock mud-sparrows
Out of the meadow clay.

So, when these all were fashioned,
And ranged in rows about,
"Now," said the little Jesus,
"We'll let the birds fly out."

Then all the happy children
Did call, and coax, and cry —
Each to his own mud-sparrow:
"Fly, as I bid you! Fly!"

But earthen were the sparrows,
And earth they did remain,
Though loud the Jewish children
Cried out, and cried again.

Except the one bird only
The little Lord Christ made;
The earth that owned him Master, —
His earth heard and obeyed.

Softly he leaned and whispered,
"Fly up to Heaven! Fly!"
And swift his little sparrow
Went soaring to the sky.

And silent all the children
Stood, awestruck, looking on,
Till, deep into the heavens,
The bird of earth had gone.

Our souls are like the sparrows
Imprisoned in the clay;
Bless Him who came to give them wings
Upon a Christmas Day!

Elizabeth Stuart Phelps

SAINT CHRISTOPHER.

Saint Christopher wished to do something to serve the King of earth and heaven; and he went to the cave of a good hermit, who said: —

"Knowest thou a certain river, stony, and wide, and deep, and often swollen by the rains, so that many perish who attempt to pass over?"

And Saint Christopher answered, "I know it."

Then said the hermit, "Go to that river, and use thy strength to aid and to save those who struggle with the stream, and those who are about to perish." To which Christopher replied joyfully, —

"This I can do."

So he went as the hermit had directed, and he dwelt by the side of the river; and having rooted up a palm-tree from the forest, — so strong he was, and tall, — he used it for a staff to support and guide his steps; and he aided those who were about to sink, and the weak he carried on his shoulders across the stream; and by day and by night he was always ready for his task, and failed not, and was never wearied of helping those who needed help.

Christopher one night heard a voice which called to him from the shore; it was the plaintive voice of a child, and it seemed to say, "Christopher, come forth and carry me over!"

And he rose and looked out, but he saw nothing: then he lay down again; but the voice called to him in the same words a second and a third time; and the third time he sought round about with a lantern; and at length he beheld a little child sitting on the bank, who entreated him, saying, —

St. Christopher.
By Orazio Borgiani, 1578-1616.

"Christopher, carry me over this night."

And Christopher lifted the child on his strong shoulders, and took his staff and entered the stream.

And the waters rose higher and higher; and the waves roared, and the wind blew; and the infant on his shoulders became heavier and heavier, till it seemed to him that he must sink under the great weight; and he began to fear. But nevertheless, taking courage, and staying his tottering steps with his palm-staff, he at length reached the opposite bank; and when he had laid the child down, safely and gently, he looked upon him with astonishment, and he said, —

"Who art thou, child, that hath placed me in such peril? Had I carried the whole world on my shoulder the burden had not been heavier!"

And the child replied: —

"Wonder not, good Christopher; for thou hast not only borne the world, but Him who made the world, upon thy shoulders. Me wouldst thou serve in this work of charity and, behold, I have accepted thy service and thee; plant thy staff in the ground, and it shall put forth leaves and fruit."

Christopher did so, and the dry staff flourished as a palm-tree in the season, and was covered with clusters of fruit; but the Christ Child had vanished from sight.

THE FIRST CHRISTMAS PRESENTS, TOLD BY E. E. HALE, AND WRITTEN OUT WITH HIS PERMISSION BY SARA E. WILTSE.

Dr. Edward Everett Hale lives in Boston, and the story of the First Christmas Presents was told by him to the children of Cottage Place Kindergarten.

He is a story-writer, a preacher, and a philanthropist. That means that he loves all kinds of people, and wants everybody and everything kindly treated.

You will hear other stories that he has told, before you have been many weeks in kindergarten.

When you go to public school, you will find Dr. Hale's stories there; and when you get to be men and women you will still love to hear them; for he writes stories that are just as interesting to grown people as to children.

THE FIRST CHRISTMAS PRESENTS.

You've all heard the story of the Father's gift to the world, of the dear Christ Child, but perhaps you never heard of the first Christmas presents the Holy Child received. You know how the wise men brought him gold and frankincense and myrrh; but these are not the presents I am going to tell you about; for there were some given before the wise men had found the manger where the Child lay. You remember he lay upon the sweet-scented hay, and a good cow looked at the Child — some people believe she knelt when she saw him. She said, "Moo, moo, moo!" as she looked, and Joseph and Mary understood her just as well as if she had spoken in their language. What do you suppose she meant to say?

I think she meant, "Dear little Christ Child, I have some milk for you." And the father Joseph brought the milk and gave some to the

Nativity (portion).

By Martin Schongauer, 1480.

babe, so that the cow made the second present on the first Christmas. We will never forget that the first was the gift of the Father to us.

After that the wise men came; but that you hear about everywhere Christmas, I hope, and many a day between.

You know, too, how soon Joseph and Mary had to take the Child and go a journey; but some other animals wanted to make gifts, and one said, "Baa, baa, baa!" Whom do you think that was?

Yes, it was the woolly sheep; and he meant that he would like to give of his wool for a warm garment to wrap the Baby in, when he should be riding in the night-time; and Mary took some of the good sheep's wool, and made a soft and pretty cloak for the Child.

So the moo-cow gave milk, and the baa-sheep gave wool.

Then when Joseph and Mary were nearly ready to start on that long journey, they heard something say, "Kit, kit, kit, ka-da-kit ! kit, kit, kit, ka-da-kit! kit, kit, kit, ka-da-kit!" What could that be?

A hen, to be sure.

And what did the hen want to give? Yes, the hen wanted the mother Mary to have a nice fresh egg for her breakfast.

Then when the Child had had some more of the moo-cow's milk, and was wrapped in the baa-sheep's wool, and Mary had eaten the hen's egg, they went out of the barn to begin their journey, and there was a donkey at the door, and he said "M-m-m-m-h — h-m — m-m-h — h-m-m-m-n m-h! m-m-m-m-h — h-m — m-m-h — h-m-m!" which meant, "I want to give Mary and the Child a ride"; and that was the best way he had of telling it. So Joseph helped the mother and Child to get upon the back of the donkey, and they rode away.

Now when we are making and receiving Christmas presents, we will remember those of the cow, the wise men, the sheep, the hen, and the donkey.

EDWARD EVERETT HALE.

Nativity.
By Martin Schongauer, 1480.

The Nativity.
By G. Bagioli.

FOURTH WEEK OF DECEMBER.

[The Christmas stories that have been already told should be repeated, — the children being encouraged to tell as much of them as they can recall. Every Christmas carol learned should be explained verse by verse by the children, not as a task, but as a bit of joyous knowledge which they joyously share with others.]

American Homestead Winter.

Published by Currier & Ives, 1868.

Happy New Year.
Published by Currier & Ives, 1876.

FIRST WEEK OF JANUARY.

WHEN are we happiest, when working for ourselves or for others? What did you do for others last month? What was done for you?

[It makes a good impression upon children to analyze with them the labor that goes to the making of one toy, — a doll, a drum, or any Christmas present they may chance to bring to kindergarten.]

CHARLOTTE AND THE TEN DWARFS.

There was once a little girl named Charlotte left alone to keep her father's house in order, and to help him in the work of the farm. The weight of care and work quite discouraged her, and not knowing what to do first, she sat down on the doorstep without doing anything. She exclaimed to herself, "Oh, why is not the good fairy Bountiful on the earth any more to help us out of our troubles?"

"Be satisfied, then; for I am here," said the fairy, close beside her.

She was an odd-looking old woman, leaning on a crutch of holly.

Charlotte asked her how she could serve her; but the fairy replied that she had come to serve and not to be served, and had brought Charlotte ten little workmen to help her. The old woman opened her cloak, and ten dwarfs of different sizes jumped out. The first two were very strong, though clumsy and awkward. "These," said the fairy, "are the strongest; the two following are taller and more skilful; the next are still taller, and one of them is especially useful in sewing, so he has a little cap called thimble; the next two have golden rings to wear, and are not easily managed alone, but have two little ones to help them. Now you will see what they can do." At a sign from the fairy the little men glided about the room, doing the coarsest and heaviest as well as finest work. At sight of this, Charlotte stretched out her arms, and begged the fairy to lend her the little dwarfs. The fairy answered that she would do better, and would give them to her, and to save trouble in carrying them with her everywhere, she would hide them in her fingers. Now you know what treasures you possess; you must keep your fingers always busy, and the work you dread so much will be done as if by magic.

Charlotte never had any trouble after this, but kept her father's house and helped in the farm work.

ANONYMOUS

Fernlike Dendritic Crystal.
A picture of a snow crystal taken
by Wilson Bentley (1865-1931).

SECOND WEEK OF JANUARY.

[Look at snowflakes on a bit of black cloth, and, if practicable, compare with other crystals; imitate the snowflakes with planes, and draw pictures of them on blackboard.

The talk may be of the difference between work of blacksmith and shoemaker, and the materials they use, and the story may be of The Blacksmith or The Shoemaker, from Prang's Pictures.]

American Railroad Scene: Snowbound.
Published by Currier & Ives, 1871.

OUR DAILY BREAD.

"AND how is Jamie?" said Robert, as he came in from his day's work, in every moment of which he had thought of his sick child. He spoke in a whisper, and in a whisper his wife answered, —

"No worse, the doctor says; and he may get well if we can get him to take enough food; but he refuses the groats and barley, and beef tea, and broth, though the spoonful of milk given him half an hour ago, he still keeps in his stomach."

This was nearly a week before Christmas.

The second day before Christmas the doctor was two hours late, because the snowdrifts were heavier than he had ever seen them in

Boston before. Robert did not come home to dinner; but he came early for his supper, and as he looked at the baby from the other side of the crib, and smiled so cheerfully, Mary felt that she could not thank God enough for his goodness.

Five-and-twenty miles away was another mother, whose baby was born the same day as Jamie. Neither mother had ever heard of the other; but we shall see how their lives were twisted together. In this country home the men were seldom home to dinner; for they were in the milk business, and had to collect the milk from the hill farms and then carry it to the milk train at three o'clock in the morning. The same day that the doctor was late to see Jamie on account of the snowdrifts in Boston, Huldah could not see the fences or woodpile, the snow was so deep about the country house, and her husband did not get home to supper until late in the night. She had shovelled a path to the barn, had given the cows and horses their supper, and milked two cows which they kept for their own use.

At nine o'clock the men came, and a story they had to tell! They had fought snow all day, had been breaking roads from farmhouses to the milk station, where the cans were piled waiting for the train that had not yet ploughed its way through the snow-banks. It was clear that no milk train nor any other train would go to Boston the next morning.

"Bad for the Boston babies," said Reuben. "Poor little things!" said Huldah.

Three o'clock in the morning Huldah's fire was burning brightly; the snow had ceased to fall at midnight, and it was now bright starlight. The men ate their breakfast, and again began the work of clearing roads, and carrying milk to the station. Huldah gave John the full milk-can into which she had poured every drop of Carry's milk, and said, "It will be one more, and God knows what child may be crying for it now."

The men worked all day, and got two hundred and thirty-nine cans one station nearer Boston, for no train had come yet. A boy of fourteen was to put on a pair of snowshoes, and get a red lantern, and stop the first train, even if it were a lightning express, and ask the conductor to take the milk to the city, no train having gone there from any direction in twenty-four hours. Silas, the boy of fourteen, walked back and forth, carrying the red lantern and listening for a train.

He sang Christmas carols, and spoke pieces, and played he was a soldier until after midnight, and then he repeated the ten commandments, and said the multiplication table, and ran up and down the track to keep himself awake. Then he thought he should surely freeze to death, the cold was so terrible, — then a globe of light swept over the valley, and the scream of an engine was welcomed by the freezing boy as if it had been an angel's whisper. "Do not stop for me," he cried, as the workmen dragged him in. "Only run slow till you are out of the ledge; we have made a milk station at the cross-road."

"Good for you!" said the fireman; and in ten seconds they were beside the pyramids of milk-cans. And the workers on the train cheered the workers at the crossroads. An empty passenger car was opened, and the milk-cans were hurried into it by forty men.

In the little house in Boston, where the sick baby lay, Christmas morning had come. Robert and Mary knelt with the other children, and said, "Our Father, who art in heaven." Mary's voice trembled a little when she came to the "daily bread," but it grew stronger as she came to the end, and could say "Thine is the power," and she believed it.

"Mamma," whispered little Fanny, as she kissed her mother after the prayer, "when I said my prayers last night, I said 'our daily milk.'"

This was more than poor Mary could bear; for last night at six o'clock the last drop of milk was sour, and Jamie could not take it.

Christmas morning Robert had been to all the neighbors, but nobody had any sweet milk. The doctor brought some condensed milk, but the sick child refused to swallow it. Kind-hearted people sent beef-tea and Scotch groats and everything they could think of that a sick child might have in place of milk, but the little boy only cried and moaned until his mother's heart was ready to break, — then the bell rang — the milkman was at the door with Huldah Stevens' own milk-can, full of rich, sweet milk, which she had sent, saying, "God knows what child may be crying for it."

Huldah never knew, though, and Mary never knew, but the good God and all good angels knew, and you and I must never forget that always our daily bread comes to us because a thousand brave men and a thousand brave women are at work praying and serving God.

E. E. HALE, in *Christmas Stories*.

The great storm of March 12th-13th.
Illustration in Frank Leslie's illustrated newspaper, Mar. 24,1888.

A STORY FOR WILLIE WINKLE.

One winter night old North Wind and little Jack Frost had a talk which I happened to overhear.

North Wind called Jack Frost to see a snowdrift which he had blown into a fence corner, and, with his gray wing, swept into curves as pretty as one ever sees anywhere except in a little child's face. Jack Frost looked and laughed, saying, "I can make things quite as pretty, but I must work in the water."

North Wind wrapped his cloak of clouds about him, and went to see Jack Frost work in a stream of water not far away.

As they flew, with clouds and snow before them, Jack Frost peeped in a window, and saw a little boy sleeping. "Let's do something for Willie Winkle," whispered Jack Frost.

"Agreed!" shouted North Wind. To work they went, North Wind puffing little starry gems of snow against the window-pane outside, while Jack Frost fastened them on, and, at the same time, drew pictures of trees and vines on the inside, which were so pretty that North Wind fairly shook the house, trying to get in to see them. Jack Frost, fearing all the noise of North Wind would waken Willie Winkle, hurriedly tasted the water in Willie's silver cup, which turned the water to ice, and crept out at the keyhole.

When North Wind and Jack Frost reached the brooklet, they were talking about the children they had seen that night; and the little brook stopped to listen, for she had missed the visits from the children for many a day. And, as she listened, every drop, ripple, and dimple of the brooklet turned to crystal, and stood still there, waiting until spring for the children.

When North Wind and Jack Frost passed a tiny pond, old North Wind fairly held his breath a moment with delight; then he, being the older, said, "Let's work together this winter."

"Agreed!" laughed Jack Frost, from the turret of an ice palace which he was finishing.

"Will you ripple the top of this water while I freeze it?"

"That I will," answered old North Wind.

"It will spoil the skating for the big boys, but we'll work for the little folks to-night."

So North Wind blew across the water till it wrinkled and waved like a broad field of wheat under the wing of South Wind in Summer. Jack Frost followed close upon the breath of North Wind, kissed the ripples and wrinkles, and there they stood.

The waters were all curled and frozen over little caves, shining grottos, and glittering palaces of ice.

As North Wind and Jack Frost were going home next morning, they saw Willie Winkle looking at the pretty pictures on his window.

"Let us speak to him," said North Wind. But at his voice the window rattled and shook so noisily that Willie Winkle ran away to sit by the warm fire.

After breakfast Willie Winkle went again to the window, and, seeing the beautiful drifts, and wreaths, and banks, and puffs of snow in corners, on gate-posts, and in tree-tops, he begged to go outside. He was no sooner in the yard than Jack Frost came creeping, and North Wind came shouting; and one pinched his ears; the other blew off his hat. And such a wrestling match as Willie Winkle had with them made even his mamma laugh.

When he went in the house, his cheeks were as red as roses, and his fingers as purple as Jack Frost could make them with his kisses and pinches.

Three children throwing snowballs.
By Otto Henry Bacher, watercolor, 1896.

THIRD WEEK OF JANUARY.

THERE is nothing so small that we may not find something very interesting in it. The story of a single grain of sand, or drop of water, or tiny snowflake, would be a long one if we could learn it, and it would take a very wise man to tell it.

[The story of The Snowflakes may be told, or that of The Carpenter, from Prang's Picture.]

THE SNOWFLAKES.

"Hurrah! We are going down to the earth," said a tiny snowflake up in its cloud home to its brothers. "I heard King Frost and the North Wind say last night that, if the East Wind would help them, they would make some more snowflakes, and send us all down to the earth."

"Oh, what fun!" cried the rest; "we will have a fine race down! I wish East Wind would hurry and bring up his clouds."

"Here he comes now!" cried a little flake.

And sure enough, far out over the ocean came the East Wind, driving the clouds filled with tiny water-drops before him.

King Frost and North Wind went to meet him when they saw him coming, and to breathe on the clouds.

Instantly the water-drops in the clouds were changed into beautiful little feathery snowflakes, which leaped joyously from their cloud home, and began their journey to the earth.

Faster and faster they came, chasing each other merrily along, and laughing gaily as the strong winds caught them and whirled them about.

"You can't catch me!" cried one.

"Don't be too sure of that!" cried another.

"I'll be there first!" called out a third.

"Not if I get there before you," laughed a fourth rushing along so swiftly that he was out of sight in an instant.

What fun it was, to be sure! and, when they finally reached the ground, how they rolled over each other and flew here and there among the leaves and bushes, till at last they were tired, and settled down to rest for awhile.

They had been quiet but a few minutes, when they heard a shout, and down the road came the schoolboys.

"Now for the fun!" said the little snowflakes. "Here come the boys to play with us!"

"A snowball match!" cried the boys. "Let's have a snowball match!"

"Yes," laughed the snowflakes, "we like that."

And so, when the boys took up the snow, the little flakes clung closely together, and did their best to make the balls quickly.

Then they laughed, and the boys laughed and shouted, as they flew.

After a short game of snowballing, the boys grew tired of this sport, and ran off to their homes to get their sleds.

So the little snowflakes had a chance to rest awhile, and to watch their brothers who were hurrying down from their cloud home to join them on earth.

"You are too late for the fun," they said to the newcomers; "we have just had a fine game of snowball with the boys."

"Oh, we shall have sport enough," they answered, "before we go off."

Just then, hearing footsteps, they looked up and saw, coming down the road, a boy who was reading as he walked slowly along.

"I wouldn't give much for that boy," said the snowflakes; "he isn't going to take any notice of us."

But when he came a little nearer to them, they heard him say this: "Without the sun there would be no vapor in the air; without the vapor there would be no clouds; and without the clouds there would be no snow; so really the sun makes the snow. That's queer, now," he added, stopping his reading and looking down at the snow at his feet. "I never knew that before."

"Well," said a snowflake, looking up, "don't you suppose there are a great many other things you don't know?"

The boy stooped down, without taking any notice of what the snowflake said, and taking some of the snow in his hand, he went on: "How soft and white you are, you snowflakes! I wish I had a magnifying-glass; then I could see your beautiful forms."

"This boy *does* take more notice of us than the other ones did," exclaimed a pleased little snowflake, "only he doesn't wish to play with us. I'll tell you how I look," he added, kindly, to the boy; "I look like a six-pointed star, and my brother looks like a six-sided plane, all covered with little sparkling dots."

The boy didn't seem to hear the snowflakes; or, perhaps he heard them, but didn't understand snow-language, so he made no reply to the speech of the little flake; but went on talking.

"Well," he said, "if the sun makes the snow for us, he takes it away from us again. I should like to know why it is that we cannot see the vapor when the sun is drawing it up through the air."

"You do see it, sometimes, you know," answered the flake, "and you call it fog. Generally you cannot see it because the particles of water which make vapor are so very, very small; so small that it takes many millions of them to make a drop of rain."

"And this vapor is rising all the time, too," the boy continued, "from the ocean, from ponds and rivers, from the ground, from plants and trees, from animals, from almost everything on the earth, and yet we know nothing about it till we see it over our heads in clouds. It is very wonderful."

"Yes, it is wonderful," replied the snowflakes; "and there are many other wonderful things happening, which you will learn about when you are older."

ANDERSEN.

Inuit village, Oopungnewing, near Frobisher Bay
on Baffin Island in the mid-19th century. c1865

Photograph shows Eskimo women and child with the photographer's wife, all in
traditional dress, sitting on the floor of an igloo, eating crabs; pair of snow shoes
and coiled rope visible in igloo. Photographed by Frank E. Kleinschmidt, 1924.

FOURTH WEEK OF JANUARY.

[Talk of the kinds of houses in which different people live, especially those in cold climates. Show pictures of Esquimaux dwellings, sleds, etc. Story of King Midas or The Cookie Boy, with a sketch of Hans Andersen if the latter is told.]

HANS CHRISTIAN ANDERSEN, the writer of the beautiful fairy stories, was born in Odense, in the island of Funen, away in the dear North country. When he was a boy he was often cold and hungry, for his father was very poor, and the little Hans had to earn money by singing in a choir to pay his teachers for every lesson he had. At last he could sing no more; he had worn such thin clothes and ragged shoes in the cold weather that his voice was spoiled with hoarseness. He tried to sell his stories, but nobody would buy them for a long, long time. At last some kind people sent him to school and paid for his lessons, but he had to go hungry in order to buy his books. Was he not a brave lad? When he grew to be a man he could write such lovely stories that people began to read them in Germany, in England, and in America, and there was no more hunger or cold for him then. Great men and famous women praised his books and were glad to do him honor, but nothing pleased him quite so much as to have the people in his native town make a great procession in his honor, and give him wreaths and strew flowers before him while they sang and shouted for joy to see him with them again. This happened when he was quite an old man, and perhaps it was the next morning that he wrote the story

King Midas.
From *A Third Reader* by Jenny H. Stickney, 1904.
Illustrated by Bonawitz.

of the Ugly Duckling, or the beginning of the true story of his life, in which he said that his life was a happy, lovely story which could not have been better if a good fairy had guided and defended him.

THE STORY OF KING MIDAS.

A great many years ago there lived a very rich king. It took him many weeks just to count his gold pieces. But he wanted all the time to be getting richer. No matter how much he had, he wanted more. He gave all his time and thought to getting gold.

One day, when he was counting his gold and looking very sad, a stranger appeared before him. "Why do you look so sad?" asked the stranger. The king answered, "Oh, if I could only turn everything I touch to gold!"

Now the stranger had a wonderful power which he could give to the king. So he said, "From tomorrow, everything you touch shall become gold."

That night the king could hardly sleep for joy. In the morning he raised his purple robe to place it on his shoulders. Instantly every thread was golden. He sat down to fasten his sandals. In a twinkling the chair in which he sat became golden. His sandals, too, the instant he touched them, changed to pure gold.

When he went for his morning walk, every flower became a golden flower. The path, and even the grass that he trod upon, became gold.

But even a king will get hungry. So Midas went back to the palace for his breakfast. We are not told what it was, but we may be sure it was a feast fit for a king. He asked for water. A glassful was given him, and the moment he put it to his lips it turned to gold.

The poor king could not drink gold. What was he to do? It was of no use to ask for another; that, too, would become gold in his hand. All the money in the world could not buy him a drink of water.

He sat down to eat. But every mouthful became gold the moment he put it to his lips. So he could eat nothing. With all his gold he would yet have to starve to death.

Then the stranger again appeared. The king, with tears in his eyes, begged him to take away the touch that turned everything to gold.

"Are you not happy, King Midas?" asked the stranger.

"I am most miserable," groaned the king. "I beg you to take away this hateful touch."

The stranger told the king to bathe in a stream near by, and the golden touch would leave him; and that water from the same stream would change back from gold anything on which he sprinkled it.

Midas lost no time in obeying. The water washed away the golden touch, but the sands of the river banks became golden, and it is said that grains of gold are to be found there to this day.

Midas was a happier king than he had ever been before.

From STICKNEY'S READER.

THE LITTLE COOKIE BOY.

Abby's mother made some little Cookie Boys. They had heads, bodies, legs, and arms. And she made two little places for eyes.

Abby watched her all the time she did it. She put them in the oven side by side and baked them to a pretty color. I will tell you the story of one of them.

He was taken out of the oven and laid on a plate on the table. It had been dark in the oven, but now it was light. He looked about and saw Abby and her brother and sister playing.

The Little Cookie Boy.
From *A Third Reader* by Jenny H. Stickney, 1904.

"Why," said he, "they are very large; but they are like me. I will ask them if they are big Cookie Boys." But Abby's mamma had forgotten to give him a mouth, so the question could not get out.

He saw Abby's aunt, who had curly hair. "I wonder if my hair is curly, too," he said. He tried to feel; but Abby's mamma had forgotten to give him any elbow-joints, or to make his shoulder-joints loose.

He tried to get up; but, poor fellow, he had no knees or hips. All he could do was to lie still and look around.

"I wonder what I was made for," he said.

Abby's mamma took him up and tied a blue ribbon around his neck. She hung him on a green tree with little lights burning all over it. The tree was load with pretty things. He began to feel quite vain. "I must be beautiful, too, or I should not be here," thought he.

One by one the things were taken from the tree. Little faces all around looked brighter as little arms became fuller.

At last our Cookie Boy was taken off and given to a merry little girl. She squeezed him so tight that he wanted to scream.

He did not think she meant to kiss him, but she put him up to her rosy mouth. He could not get away for he had no joints, and if he had had joints he would have walked or run into that pretty, rosy mouth, for a Cookie Boy likes nothing so well as to be eaten by a good-natured, happy little boy or girl. As it was, he had to wait to be eaten one arm and one leg at a time; but the kind-hearted little girl kept his head until the very last, so that his little eyes had the fun of seeing himself eaten by the rosy mouth; and he looked so pleased when his head was on its way to her pretty teeth, that she called her brother and gave him just half of it, and he had kept part of his Cookie Boy for her; so there were four happy children, the two that ate and the two that were eaten.

ANDERSEN *(adapted)*.

Flag of Admiral of the Fleet.
GREAT BRITAIN.

Admiral's Flag
FRANCE.

Imperial Standard.
GERMANY.

Admirals Flag
ITALY.

Admiral's Flag.
SPAIN.

Royal Flag.
SWEDEN.

From *Flags of Maritime Nations.*
United States Navy Dept. Bureau of Navigation, 1882.

FIRST WEEK OF FEBRUARY.

[Talk with the children about the countries represented in the kindergarten, Germany, Ireland, and America, with especial reference to great or good men of the various nations; fac-similes of their flags, or pictures of their national flowers or shields may be shown. Tell the children of the holiday to be enjoyed this month on account of one of America's great men.]

Scene in cotton field.

HELPS TO AN OBJECT LESSON ON CALICO PRINT.

[Have the children find articles of clothing made of these materials. A plain white handkerchief is a very good thing to observe first.]

IN the warm countries (where the Brown Baby and the Black Baby live) the people plant little black seeds in the ground. The sun and the rain help the little seeds to send roots downward and leaves and stems upward. When the stems are about two feet high (measuring from the floor with the hand) they have pretty yellow flowers; after the flowers fade and fall there is left in their places small green pods or pockets that look much like green nuts. After a few weeks of sunshine and a few showers of warm rain, the soft green pockets become hard and brown, and at last they break open and out of each pops a bunch of white cotton like this. [Show a cotton pod.]

The field of cotton then looks as if a snowball had fallen upon every stem. Men, women, and children go with baskets to gather the cotton, which is put in a machine which picks out every little seed hidden in the white bunches, after which it is sent away in ships and steam-cars to be made into — what? Yes; cloth for aprons and dresses and pillow-slips, etc.

[Be careful to keep the children to cotton materials, excluding linen.]

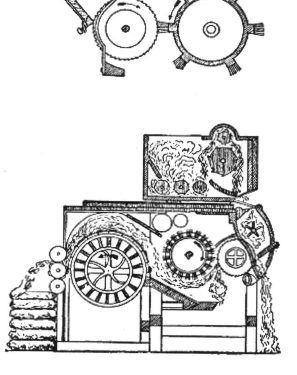

Cotton Gin.
From *Textiles* by William H. Dooley, 1910.

In the great mills where cotton is made into cloth, they put it between rollers that are covered with wire teeth which pick it to pieces, take out every speck of dirt, and press it into such strips as this : —

[Any teacher can get samples from cotton mills, with a little trouble.]

Card Room.
From *Textiles* by William H. Dooley, 1910.

These long ribbon-like strips are drawn through rollers that press and pull them until they are as fine as this. [Show sample of third process.]

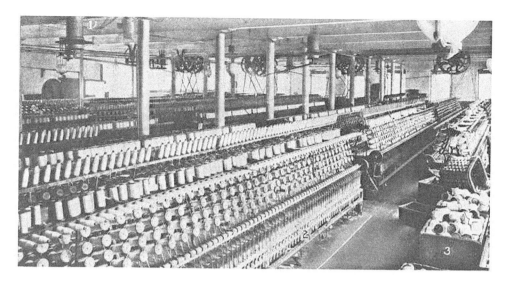

Twisting Room.
From *Textiles* by William H. Dooley, 1910.

Now the cotton is ready to be twisted into four threads; this twisting is called spinning, and as the machines twist or spin it they roll it upon spindles like this. [Show a spindle of cotton.]

It is now ready to be woven into cloth, and is put into machines that draw a great many threads from these spindles, laying them close together from front to back. Another thread is wound upon a shuttle, and a machine sends this thread through the others, over one, under one, over one, under one, faster than you can say it, so fast that the little shuttle looks like a bird flying so swiftly that one cannot see the tiny thread he carries back and forth, from left to right and from right to left.

This is called weaving cloth. Here are some bits of coarse cotton cloth from which you may pull the threads to see that they are woven over one and under one, as I have told you.

Girls at weaving machine. Lincoln Cotton Mills, Evansville, Ind.
Photographed by Lewis Wickes Hine, 1908.

Another day, if you can tell me about the growth of cotton, and the making of thread, of which the plain cloth is made, I will tell you how the bright colors are put on the cloth to make the pretty colored prints for your dresses.

If some little girl wishes to do so, she may bring me a piece of her dress, and I will try to tell about its manufacture.

Washington Crossing the Delaware.
By Emanuel Leutze, 1898.

SECOND WEEK OF FEBRUARY.

[Show the children a portrait of General Washington, and tell them on what day he was born. Tell them why all schools are closed on his birthday, and dwell upon the childhood that foreshadowed the nobility of the man. The story of George Washington and his Hatchet is not trite to the children, and their interest in it and their pencil sketches of the boy, the tree, and the hatchet, with a little dramatic effort on the part of the teacher, will redeem the old tale from the contempt which is felt for it in some places. The marked moral effect upon children of this old story of truthfulness ought to be reason enough for its restoration to its rightful place in children's literature.

A brief sketch of the Washington Elm, and the regard shown for it by Cambridge citizens, is both entertaining and instructive.

Washington crossing the Delaware has wrought upon the imaginations of children in a remarkable manner. For weeks the painted circle on the floor has been the Delaware River to them, and the floor has been gay with paper boats in which imaginary heroes were obeying the commands of General George Washington!]

HELPS TO OBJECT LESSON ON CALICO AND PRINT.

No. 2.

AFTER the threads, about which we talked before, are woven into cloth, the cloth has to be made white by boiling and bleaching. You will see that the thread on the spindle is yellow-white, and so is the scrap of unbleached cloth. This kind of cloth is used in making most of your underclothes.

CALICO.

[The teacher should have a bit of calico, which is different in texture from cotton sheeting, and is known in commerce as calico until it is printed with colors, when it becomes "print."]

Here is a piece of cloth which was woven on purpose for dresses; these threads are spun and woven a little differently from the threads used in making common cotton cloth.

As soon as it is woven, it is run through a machine, which clips or shears off every thread that sticks up; then it is run very swiftly over a little blaze of gas, which burns off every fibre of the cotton which would make it look hairy and uneven. The first process they call shearing and the second one singeing the cloth.

After it is sheared and singed, it is bleached until it is as white as this you see in my hand.

It is now put into the machine for printing figures upon it.

[The simpler the pattern, and the smaller the number of colors, the better for a first lesson.]

The description here given is of an elaborate pattern.

Figures are cut in a copper roller just the shape of all the red spots in this piece of calico; red dyestuff, much like red paste, is spread upon the roller, after which the roller is scraped with a sharp knife as it turns round, the knife taking off every bit of paste except that which sinks into the little holes cut in the copper roller; the white calico, which is run between this pictured and pasted roller and a smooth one, comes out with red figures on it, having taken the red paste out of the little holes in the copper roller. The calico must now go between rollers cut with figures like all these pink ones; and what colored paste should go into these holes in the roller? Pink paste, of course; and when this calico, with red figures, has been run between the rollers with pink paste in its patterns, how many colors will you see in the cloth?

Two; red and pink. After the red and pink figures are stamped upon the white cloth, it must pass between rollers with shapes of the blue figures cut in the copper of one roller, with blue paste in the forms; then it must go over a roller with leaves and other forms cut upon it, in which the green paste is put. Last of all comes a roller with all the shapes which you see in brown cut upon it; and after the calico goes over this roller, there is but little of the white left. You can see the little white lines and dots that are left uncolored. Can any little boy or girl tell how all these white lines could have been colored purple? A copper roller would have been cut full of little holes, just like these white lines and dots, and purple paste would have been put in the holes, and the cloth run between this roller and a smooth one.

Of course the calico gets wet with all this colored paste; but as fast as it comes from between the rollers, it is carried by a large roller into a room kept so hot that nobody can go into it, where it dries very fast, and the heat makes the colors stay in the cloth. This hot room has glass sides, and people can look in and see the calico coming in at the floor, and going out at the roof, as fast as it rolls from the copper cylinders below. All the time the strips of calico are kept smooth and straight, for they are not cut into pieces until they are perfectly dry; then a woman tends a machine which folds the calico into pieces that are cut off and pressed into the neat package which you see on the shelves of the stores.

Some girls sew the ends of these packages together, and others paste the name of the mills at which the cloth is made on one side of the package, after which they are wrapped in paper, and sent to all the cities and villages where there are little girls to wear dresses — and that is pretty nearly the world over, is it not?

Calicoes of but one color are dyed, not printed.

Betsy Ross, 1777.
By J.L.G. Ferris.

THIRD WEEK OF FEBRUARY.

[Especial attention may be drawn to the stars and stripes, and the children can easily comprehend that there was no such flag when Washington was a little boy; but when America became a self-governing country, it had to have a flag of its own. The children will be much interested in a little information about national courtesies, as shown by the display of flags, in the rules governing the flags in foreign waters; the bravery of men who have upheld the flag of our nation under great difficulties and dangers. They would also be interested in the first United States flag raised on land, and in Paul Jones' United States flag, the first raised on an American war vessel at sea. See Winsor's "America" and Preble's "History of the United States Flag." The points are given in the "Leading Facts of American History," Ginn & Co., pp. 175 (note 3) and 178.

A review of salient points of whatever has been told them of the history of Washington. Much of their block-building, drawing, sewing, and other occupations may be closely connected with facts of history.]

Washington Delivering His Inaugural Address.
April 1789, in the old City Hall, New York.
painted by T.H. Matteson, 1849.

FOURTH WEEK OF FEBRUARY.

[The children should be led to tell how they spent the holiday, and what they saw or heard that made them think of General Washington.]

AMY STEWART.

THERE was once a girl named Amy Stewart, who liked to play all day in the garden among the flowers and birds. She said they talked to her.

One day her mother said, "You are old enough now, Amy, to do a little work, and you must begin early to be industrious."

"O mamma! I do not like to work; may I not go in the woods and play before I begin to work?"

"As I have nothing ready for you to do just now, you may go for a little while," said her mother.

So Amy ran out of doors. A pretty Gray Squirrel ran across her path, and she called to him, saying, —

"Dear Squirrel, you have nothing to do but play and eat nuts, have you?"

"Yes," said Mr. Squirrel, "I have a large family to support, and I am busy laying up nuts for the winter, so I cannot stop to play with you."

Just then a Bee came buzzing by. Amy said, —

"Little Bee, do you have any work to do?"

"It seems to me I have no time for anything but work, getting honey and making the honeycomb."

Amy now saw an Ant carrying a crumb of bread.

"Is not that crumb too heavy for you? I wish you would drop it and play with me."

"It is heavy, but I am too glad to get it not to be willing to carry it; but I will stop long enough to tell you about a lazy day we once had. Our house was destroyed and I was too lazy to help rebuild it; and I said to my brothers, 'Let us go and travel; perhaps we will find a house ready-made; perhaps the butterflies will play with us.' We travelled a long way, but we found no ready made house, and at last were obliged to build one for ourselves. Since then we have been contented to do all the work that we find necessary." The Ant then picked up the crumb of bread and hurried away.

Amy sat down on a stone and thought: "It seems to me all creatures have some work to do, and they seem to like it; but I do not believe Flowers have anything to do." So she walked up to a Red Poppy, and said, —

"Beautiful Red Poppy, do flowers work?"

"Of course we do," said the Poppy. "I have to take great care to gather all the red rays the good Sun sends down to me, and I must keep them in my silken petals for you to use, and the green rays must be untangled and held by my glossy leaves, and my roots must drink water, my flowers must watch the days not to let the seed-time pass by — ah, my child, I assure you we are a busy family, and that is why we are so happy."

Amy walked slowly homeward and said to her mother: —

"The Squirrels, Bees, Ants, and even the Flowers have something to do. I am the only idle one; please give me some work to do."

Then her mother brought her a towel to hem, which she had begun so long before that she had quite forgotten it. She worked very faithfully and grew to be an industrious woman, never forgetting that work makes us happier than idleness.

ANONYMOUS.

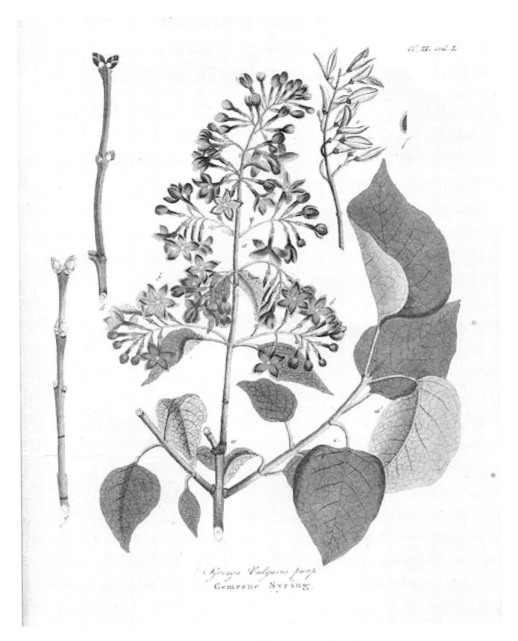

Syringa Vulgaris (Common Lilac).

From *Deutschlands Flora in Abbildungen*.

By Johann Georg Sturm (Painting by Jacob Sturm), 1796.

FIRST WEEK OF MARCH.

WE have talked about the animals that went to sleep in the fall and remained sleeping all winter. Some of the plants have been asleep, too, and a few of them are just beginning to waken. We could hurry some of the little buds by bringing them in by the fire, and placing them in water when the sun shines.

[Lilac leaves are easily forced, as well as cherry blossoms and pussy willows.

Attention may be called to the little scale of willow bud, which children love to call the baby willow's blanket, which it throws off when the sun begins to warm all things.

A chestnut-leaf bud and hickory-leaf bud may be shown with their furry coats for winter wear. The flow of sap in spring, giving juice to the buds, may be explained, and the extra supply which the maple-tree furnishes, in which there is such quantities of sugar for children as well as for leaf-buds.

A bit of maple sugar for each child helps to impress these facts upon the minds of the little ones.]

HELPS TO AN OBJECT LESSON ON PAPER.

[This must always be preceded by the lesson on Cotton Cloth.]

The Thrasher.*

The Sorting and Shedding Room.

Can any child tell what is done with our dresses, and aprons, and all our clothes that are made of cotton or linen, when they are quite worn out?

Yes; the ragman takes them; but what do you think he can do with them? He sells them to the people who have paper mills.

---

* All pictures from *The Story of Paper-Making: An Account of Paper-Making from Its Earliest Known Record Down to the Present Time*, by Frank O. Butler, 1901.

In these mills the rags are thrown into a great machine with rollers that are covered with little teeth or knives that tear the rags all to bits; they are washed and boiled until all the color comes out; then they are ground and washed again until they are white and fine like this. [Show a bit of pulp.]

Rags in various stages.

Rag pulp.

We cannot call this pretty, white stuff calico, or even rags, any more, can we? It has a new name now: pulp.

Great quantities of this pulp mixed with clear water are carried over sieves by machinery, and as it runs over the sieves the water runs through, and a thin sheet of pulp runs across the sieve into rollers that press it into a firmer shape; it is paper; but it is so wet that it must be rolled between hot iron rollers to dry it. When it comes out of these rollers it is like this. [Show a sheet of undressed paper.]

The Rag Cutters.   The Washers and Beaters.

The sheets of paper that come out of the rollers are as wide as three of our kindergarten tables, and so long that the end does not appear as long as the mill wheels keep turning; but a woman cuts off large strips as fast as she can pile them up. To make smooth writing-paper, something like starch is put into the paper as it runs through the rollers.

The men who gather the rags from house to house cannot find enough in all the cities and country to make as much paper as we need, so the paper-makers have to use something else with the rags. Of course they look for something that grows out of doors, as the cotton and flax does. What can it be?

WOOD.

Yes; they use more wood now than rags. They chop and saw trees into small pieces, which are ground and washed until they are like this. [Show wood pulp.] What shall we call it?

PULP.

Sometimes they make paper of this alone.

The wood is so good for paper-making, and they can get so much of it, for they use three kinds, poplar, spruce, and pine, that there is very little paper used now-a-days that has not a considerable quantity of wood in it.

[The children will almost know, without being told, that silk and wool cannot be made into paper.]

The Modern Fourdrinier Machine.

The First Press Rolls.

The Size Tub.

SECOND WEEK OF MARCH.

WE had something sweet to eat last week; does anybody remember what it was? In what was the sugar found?

[Show a cube of loaf sugar, and encourage the children to note the difference between it and a cube of maple sugar. Tell them that this sugar is also found in the sap or juice of a plant, and give them a short account of the process of extracting the juice from sugar-cane, and boiling it until the water goes off in steam, leaving the sugar in the kettles. Show them a beet, and tell them the little sugar grains are hidden in its juices; but not so well concealed but that the sugar finders get it, and sell a great deal of beet sugar in some parts of the world. Any personal experience of the teacher in a sugar-orchard will be hailed with delight, and a little maple syrup may be boiled in the presence of the children, over an alcohol or kerosene stove, and the evaporation noticed; with a little trouble a valuable object lesson may be combined with a story of the process of sugar manufacturing.]

Slitting and Winding.

Blowpipes Cooling Calender Rolls.

The Supercalenders.

Cutting from the Roll.

Sorting of Finished Sheets.

The Hydraulic Press.

SECOND LESSON, OR REVIEW OF PAPER—MAKING.

[Show a bit of paper, and ask of what it is made. Show colored paper, and tell how the dye is put into the wet pulp.]

The papers used for paper-folding in kindergarten, that are colored only on one side, are so colored by putting colored paste on one side of the sheet of white paper as it passes between the rollers.

Coarse brown paper is made of old hemp carpets, and often of straw.

[Ask the children to bring bits of paper, and let them compare kinds and colors and tell, if they can, how it is that some paper is colored on one side only, and some is colored through and through. Nothing fixes facts in their minds like investigation for themselves, and the child who brings its own bit of paper is likely to remember about that particular kind of paper.

It will not injure the samples of pulp to put them in water, if great care is taken that the water is clear and the sample thoroughly and quickly dried before putting away.

No teacher should make incorrect statements about growths or manufactures. If she does not know the exact truth about any question asked by the children, by all means let her say she does not know, but she will try to find out, and then let her be cautious about her authority. She should know, and know that she knows, before telling what kind of wood or metal she handles.]

Rubber tree of commerce.
Published by Detroit Publishing Co., 1900-1906.

THIRD WEEK OF MARCH.

WE have learned a great deal about the sap of the maple-tree.
People used to believe that in every tree there was hidden a beautiful
woman; and they thought she was singing when the wind sighed

among the branches, or that they heard her dress rustle when the evening breeze stirred the leaves. We have learned that these people made a mistake about these things; but they made none in thinking the trees were beautiful in every part.

You have learned some of the uses of various kinds of trees. Some furnish sugar, and some the strong timbers for ships; some give us broad leaves for fans, and others supply us with fruits and nuts. There are some trees that grow in great numbers in South America that bear no fruit or nuts for us; but they are as full of milk-white juice as our maple-trees are full of clear sap; they are bored much as our maple-trees are, and the thick, white juice is gathered in pails, and smoked until the water is nearly evaporated; then it is taken in great, dark-colored, smoky lumps, and piled into ships, and brought to New York and Boston, and put into the rubber factories; for the milk-white sap is rubber, and the tree that gives it to us is the rubber-tree. Bring in some of your overshoes and waterproofs, and we will see what other things in the room came from the rubber-tree.

[The teacher may have at hand a leadpencil, with rubber eraser, a bit of elastic ribbon, some rubber bands, etc., allowing the children to "find" these things, and ask questions about them.

The story of Kitty Caoutchouc may be told in this connection.

The First Object Lesson on Rubber may precede the story of Kitty Caoutchouc.]

HELPS TO OBJECT LESSONS ON RUBBER.

[Begin by asking the children to find as many things as they can that are made of rubber; the result will probably be a pair of overshoes, a rubber ball, an eraser, and the chair tips. Some kindergartens have a rubber doll, and some a rubber cow;

but it would be better to have the children think about rubber a week after this lesson, and bring their own samples of manufactured rubber, for the second lesson, than to give them too many things at once.]

Man holding ball of rubber on stick over fire
(between 1890 and 1923).

The rubber-tree grows in all very hot countries. Such as those in which the Brown Baby and the Black Baby live. It is a tall, slender tree, with leaves shaped much like our chestnut leaves, though having smooth edges, and being much thicker and more glossy than any of the leaves in this country.

Men bore holes in the rubber-trees, and put in faucets — and what runs out of the faucet? No, not water, but milk; the milk is not good to drink, and it is thick like cream, and sticks like molasses. The men take some sticks covered with clay, and dip them in these pails of rubber milk, and then hold them in smoke until the milk turns stiff like warm molasses candy; then they dip the stick in the milk again. Every time the stick is dipped in the milk, some of it clings, until there is as much on the stick as a man can lift; the stick, being covered with clay, is easily pulled out, but the clay stays in; these great bunches of hardened rubber milk are put in ships and sent to the rubber factories in Boston and New York, and other large cities.

When the milk stops running from the faucet, another hole is bored in the tree, and the faucet put in the new place, until the tree has been milked three times; when it is left to rest three years to make more milk.

This hardened milk is rubber, all smoky, you remember, and here is a piece of it (No. 1), which a man sawed off for us. In the rubber factory, they put these great lumps of rubber against saws, that whirl very fast, and saw them up into such cakes as this (No. 1); and then it is put in a machine and chopped as fine as hash, after which the smoke and clay are washed out, until it is white as milk again. This piece (No. 2) has been washed and chopped, but it turns dark by staying in the light. The day it was taken from the rubber factory it was white as wool.

After being washed and chopped fine, it is pressed out in thin sheets, and put away to get perfectly dry, which takes many months.

Bales of plantation rubber
(between 1890 and 1923).

When it is dry it is ready to be pressed into balls; but other things have to be mixed with it to make it gray, yellow, or brown, as you see it in things made of rubber; for it will always turn black unless something is put in to make it another color.

[Samples of rubber, as numbered above, are in the Cabinet of the Boston Kindergartens, for use of the teachers.]

KITTY CAOUTCHOUC.

Once upon a time a little princess was going on a journey with her papa and mamma, the king and queen of Nowhere–land. When the little princess had filled her little trunk with her little shoes, little hats, and little gloves, and the little horses and carriage were quite ready for her to start, she sat down on the steps of the palace and began to cry so loudly that the king and queen and all the servants, and all the children who had been staring at the little carriage, gathered about her, all asking at once, —

"Why does your little highness cry?"

The little princess put her little fists in her little eyes and cried louder than before. One of the street children offered her a bit of sticky candy from his pocket, but she sobbed, "I have six pounds of candy in my trunk; I do not cry for candy!"

The king turned away and wiped his eyes, after which he offered her a gold piece; but she did not stop crying, though she put one of her little fists in her little pocket and made the little gold pieces jingle rather angrily, while she sobbed, "I have gold pieces; it is not for gold I cry."

A servant came running toward her with a plate of cake; but the little princess would have none of it, for she had eaten nothing all day but cake, and when had they ever seen her cry for cake?

The queen called a doctor who was riding past, and the doctor took a bottle of medicine from his case; but the little princess shut her teeth and muttered that she was not ill, and would not cry for medicine if she were.

A Morning Walk, 1898.

Then the queen sat down on the steps and covering her eyes with a lace handkerchief began to cry almost as piteously as the princess herself, and they might have been crying yet but for a dear old grandma who happened to be passing, and said, —

"Bless her heart, I know what she wants," — and taking off her own apron she rolled it up, pinned her silk handkerchief around it for a shawl, and placed it in the arms of the princess, who stopped crying, hugged the doll in her arms, climbed into the carriage, and rode joyfully away.

The doll was named Caro Calicut because she was made of calico, and she and the princess rode many miles together; but the pins would fall out of the shawl, and the body would spread itself out like a sail in the carriage, or tumble itself out of all human shape when it was supposed to be sleeping beside the princess, until the little mother grew tired of asking Caro Calicut where she had left her feet, and what had become of her face.

One day the little princess sat down upon the pavement in the great city of Paris, and wiping her eyes with Caro Calicut's red silk shawl, she cried, "Now where is Caro Calicut herself?"

No one could answer.

The king said perhaps the ragman had her, and the queen said perhaps she had sailed away on the wind.

Then the little princess cried louder than before, and the king ran away as fast as he could, returning in a few minutes with a doll almost as large as the princess herself.

This doll had real hair and blue eyes; her cheeks were rosy, and her arms were plump and were so jointed that the doll could be made to put her hands over her eyes or behind her head. The little princess stopped crying, kissed the new doll, and named her Semiramis Cera, because she was made of wax.

The princess and Semiramis Cera had many happy hours together, but one warm day the princess forgot to provide a sunshade for Semiramis Cera, who sat with the driver all day, and at night she had the measles, — at least the princess called the disorder of her face the measles, and neither the king nor queen corrected her; the maid said it was a mercy it was not small-pox.

Caro Calicut had been found the day after the purchase of Semiramis Cera, and as the little princess refused to leave either of the dolls at a hospital, an ambulance was purchased in which the dolls rode after the royal family for fear the new member would take the measles or have a spasm when Caro Calicut should go through with some of her transformations.

The new member was made of china and was therefore named Carrie Ceramics; but Carrie Ceramics fell out of the carriage just as it was going over the narrow road between North and South America, and in the fall her arm was broken and she had to be removed to the ambulance; so the poor little princess rode toward Para with empty arms. I must say that the dolls in the ambulance appeared very well and happy, and were quite as attentive to the scenery as they were before the accidents.

The royal family soon drove into a country where the flowers were very large and brilliant; the trees had leaves thicker than our dinner-plates and greener than the greenest leaves of the greenest June you ever saw. At last the trees made the roads quite impassable for carriages, and the royal family concluded to walk a little way; but the princess would not leave her family behind, nor would she trust them to maids or coachmen, so the king carried Caro Calicut, the queen carried Semiramis Cera, and the princess led Carrie Ceramics by the arm which was not broken.

They had not walked far when they met a little black girl carrying a doll whose arms would not break though she should fall from a house-roof, nor would she get the measles by riding all day in the sun, nor would she resolve herself into elements if pins and strings were lost, or dissolve if she were left in the bath-tub all day.

The entire party sat down in the shade of a rubber-tree, and the little black girl introduced her doll — Katharina Caoutchouc — to Carrie Ceramics, Semiramis Cera, and Cara Calicut.

As a matter of course the little princess did not leave South America without a rubber doll.

FOURTH WEEK OF MARCH.

DO you know from what the maple-tree grows?

What tree would grow from an apple seed?

What tree would grow from an acorn?

What tree would grow from an orange seed?

Our plants grow from seeds, and before the frost is out of the earth, so that we can plant flower seeds out in the gardens; we will plant some in the boxes or flower pots in the house.

[The teacher may direct the planting of nasturtiums, morning-glories, etc.]

We want to see how they grow; but if we dig them up every day, we shall spoil them; so when we put some in the earth, we will put others in this sponge where we can see what they do.

[Place a sponge in a glass which is narrower at the bottom than the top, and put in water until it is within an inch of the sponge; tuck some seeds in the pores of the sponge, taking care that the water is supplied as it evaporates. As the seeds sprout, have the children name the parts, — roots, stem, and leaves.

Story of Cotton Cloth and Paper, the Story of the Gardener, from Prang's picture, the Story of the Pea-Blossom, or Second Object Lesson on Rubber, may be given.]

SECOND LESSON ON RUBBER.

Specimens of manufactured rubber are supplied in the box marked "Second Lesson on Rubber," to be given after the children are impressed with the fact that the rubber is not made in the factory.

The water-proof qualities of the rubber may be shown by pouring a cup of water in the muslin bag and then trying the same experiment with the water-proof bag. Perhaps this will help the children to remember their overshoes on rainy days.

The rubber is spread upon the cloth by running them both through hot iron rollers.

The elasticity of the rubber can be shown by passing the tape and elastic band to the children, letting them make their own experiments. Some of them will be likely to measure the unstretched band and then the stretched band on the tables.

These elastic ribbons are made by stretching the little rubber threads as long as they can be stretched, and then weaving in a silk or cotton thread until a long ribbon is made; of course, as soon as it is unfastened at the ends it draws up as we see it.

Lead the children to tell of as many things that are made of rubber as they can. A picture of each article not in the room might be drawn upon the board.

Pillows and cushions, little red balloons, hose-pipes, erasers, water-proofs, and overshoes are the most common things.

Pen-holders, knife-handles, buttons, combs, and bracelets are made of rubber by adding something to it to make it harder.

Even boats and bottles are made of it.

A man told me that our rubber balls are all made in New York and our dolls in France.

THE PEA-BLOSSOM.

There were once five peas in one shell; they were green, and the shell was green, and so they believed that the whole world must be green also, which was a very natural conclusion.

The shell grew and the peas grew; they accommodated themselves to their position, and sat all in a row. The sun shone without and warmed the shell, and the rain made it clear and transparent; it was mild and agreeable in broad daylight and dark at night, as it generally is; and the peas, as they sat there, grew bigger and bigger, and more thoughtful as they mused, for they felt there must be something for them to do.

"Are we to sit here forever?" asked one; "shall we not become hard by sitting so long? There must be something outside; I feel sure of it."

And so weeks passed by; the peas became yellow, and the shell became yellow.

"All the world is turning yellow, I suppose," said they, — and perhaps they were right.

Suddenly they felt a pull at the shell; it was torn off, and held in human hands, then slipped into the pocket of a jacket, in company with other full pods.

"Now we shall soon be let out," said one, — just what they all wanted.

"I should like to know which of us will travel farthest," said the smallest of the five; "we shall soon see now."

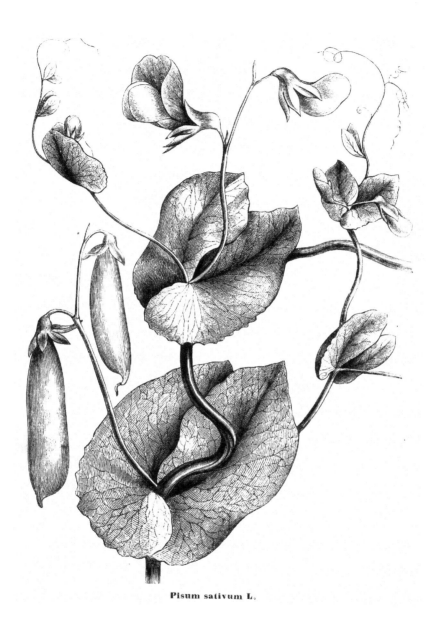

Pisum sativum L.

Pisum Sativum (Pea).
From *Botanische Unterhaltungen zum Verständniß der heimathlichen Flora*
(Botanical Conversations to the Understanding of the Native Flora), 1858.

"What is to happen will happen," said the largest pea.

"Crack!" went the shell as it burst, and the five peas rolled out into the bright sunshine. There they lay in a child's hand. A little boy was holding them tightly; he said they were fine peas for his pea-shooter. And immediately he put one in and shot it out.

"Now I am flying out into the wide world," said the pea; "catch me if you can;" and he was gone in a moment.

"I," said the second, "intend to fly straight to the sun; that is a shell that lets itself be seen, and it will suit me exactly;" and away he went.

"Wherever we find ourselves we will go to sleep," said the two next; "we shall still be rolling onwards;" and they did certainly fall on the floor, and roll about before they got into the pea-shooter; but they were put in for all that. "We will go farther than the others," said they.

"What is to happen will happen," exclaimed the last, as he was shot out of the pea-shooter; and as he spoke he flew up against an old board under a garret window, and fell into a little crevice, which was almost filled up with moss and soft earth. The moss closed itself about him, and there he lay a captive indeed, but not unnoticed by God.

"What is to happen will happen," said he to himself.

Within the little garret lived a poor woman, who went out to clean stoves, and do such hard work; for she was strong and industrious. Yet she remained always poor; and at home in the garret lay her only daughter, not quite grown up, and very delicate and weak. For a whole year she had kept her bed.

Quietly and patiently she lay all the day long, while her mother was away from home at her work.

Spring came, and early one morning the sun shone brightly through the little window, and threw his rays over the floor of the room. Just as the mother was going to her work, the sick girl fixed her gaze on the lowest pane of the window.

"Mother!" she exclaimed, "what can that little green thing be that peeps in at the window? It is moving in the wind." The mother stepped to the window and half opened it. "Oh!" she said. "There is actually a little pea that has taken root and is putting out its green leaves. How could it have got into this crack? Well, now, here is a little garden for you to amuse yourself with." So the bed of the sick girl was drawn nearer to the window, that she might see the budding plant; and the mother went out to her work.

"Mother, I believe I shall get well," said the sick child in the evening; "the sun has shone in here so brightly and warmly today and the little pea is thriving so well; I shall get on better, too, and go out into the warm sunshine again."

"God grant it!" said the mother. She propped up with a little stick the green plant which had given her child such pleasant hopes of life, so that it might not be broken by the winds; she tied the piece of string to the window-sill and to the upper part of the frame, so that the pea-tendrils might twine round it when it shot up. And it did shoot up; indeed, it might almost be seen to grow from day to day.

"Now really here is a flower coming," said the mother one morning. She remembered that for some time the child had spoken more cheerfully, and during the last few days had raised herself in bed in the morning to look with sparkling eyes at her little garden which contained but a single pea-plant.

A week later the invalid sat up for the first time a whole hour, feeling quite happy by the open window in the warm sunshine, while outside grew the little plant, and on it a pink pea-blossom in full bloom. The little maiden bent down and gently kissed the delicate leaves. This day was like a festival to her.

"Our heavenly Father himself has planted that pea, and made it grow and flourish, to bring joy to you and hope to me, my blessed child," said the happy mother, and she smiled at the flower.

But what became of the other peas? Why, the one who flew out into the wide world, and said, "Catch me if you can," fell into a gutter on the roof of a house, and ended his travels in the crop of a pigeon. The two lazy ones were carried quite as far, for they also were eaten by pigeons, so they were at least of some use; but the fourth, who wanted to reach the sun, fell into a sink, and lay there in the dirty water for days and weeks, till he had swelled to a great size.

"I am getting beautifully fat," said the pea; "I expect I shall burst at last; no pea could do more than that, I think; I am the most remarkable of all the five which were in the shell."

But the young maiden stood at the open garret window, with sparkling eyes and the rosy hue of health upon her cheeks, and folded her thin hands over the pea-blossom, thanking God for what he had done.

ANDERSEN.

Wisconsin — Appleton Paper Mills.
1898.

CLOTH AND PAPER STORY.

[Story that may be told after the lessons on Cloth and Paper.]

Beside a large field stood three trees, — a, very tall poplar-tree, a middle-sized pine-tree, and a tiny little spruce-tree. In the field grew many hundred little plants; they were about as high as our tables here in the kindergarten. One morning the plants had many thousands of straw-colored flowers. The tall poplar-tree wished he had flowers as large for him as the straw-colored ones were for the little plants; and the middle-sized pine-tree sighed and wished he had some kind of flowers in place of so many millions of leaves like green needles; and the tiny little spruce-tree said it would be very pleasant these hot days to carry flowers that looked like straw-colored silk parasols.

(The blossom of the cotton plant is much like a small single hollyhock.)

One morning when they awoke, all the pretty straw-colored flowers had turned pink, and the trees looked on in great wonder, and then looked at their own leaves to see if they too had changed color in the night, but every leaf was as green as it was the day before. But the little plants did not stop to look at themselves or even at the tall trees, but kept at their work day and night, until the sun and the rain and the wind had faded, spoiled, and torn their pink parasol flowers all to bits, and they were thrown on the ground, to be of use there. The stems or handles the plants still held quite upright, and in a few days there were little green pockets with pretty fringes around them, growing just where the parasol flowers had been. The trees were greatly pleased with the little workers, and cried: "Hurrah for you, little plants! I wonder what you carry in your pockets!"

Very soon the green pockets turned brown and popped open, every one showing *a little ball of snow-white cotton.*

The field looked then as if a storm of ready–made snowballs had fallen upon the plants.

While they were standing there, some children came out to play kindergarten under the three trees, and they said something about having a motto; and the motto was just one little word, — HELP.

When the children went away, the trees and plants agreed that they would have the same motto since it seemed to make the children so happy. Then they laughed at themselves and wondered how they could help anybody even if they knew of any one who needed help.

We shall see.

Very soon some people came with baskets and picked all the white balls of cotton, and every time they carried a basketful past the trees, the cotton would whisper, "Remember our motto is Help." And the trees would answer, "Our motto is Help; we shall meet again somewhere."

The cotton was taken to a mill and made into cloth for children's dresses, and the dresses were nearly worn out when a man went to the field and chopped down the tall poplar–tree, and the middle-sized pine-tree, and the tiny spruce-tree. After chopping them down he sawed them into little pieces and took them to a mill. The calico dresses were quite worn out now, and having been sold to the ragman, were put in a cart and taken to the very same mill, so that one man was tossing a bundle of rags into one door while another was tossing the bits of wood in at another.

In one great boiler, there in the mill, the bits of cloth were torn and boiled and ground to pulp. In another great boiler in the mill the bits of wood were torn and boiled and ground into pulp, and at last they met in a great box — wood and rags as white as snow.

Somebody went into the mill, and said, "What a noisy place!" But a little boy said, —

"I hear something besides noise.

"Just listen to the water, and the wheels, and the bands; and the saws, and the knives! They are all singing, 'Help, help'" Something else was repeating this motto deep down in the box where the cotton pulp and wood pulp were dancing and whirling in the water. True enough; they had found each other and were being made into something both useful and pretty.

"Paper!"

Yes, they were being made into paper, and this is what was written on the paper: —

Help, help, help! Help with a will.
Help in field and help in mill;
Whether you are child or man,
Tree or plant, you must and can
Help, help, help!

FIRST WEEK OF APRIL.

[The children may be led to closer observation of roots. Potatoes, turnips, and carrots may be drawn. A few grains of wheat sowed in a sponge, as above directed, afford a beautiful specimen of thread-roots.

The story of Baby Calla may be told.

If there is any disagreeable tendency to observe All Fools' Day, a little conversation about the history of the day, and its general observation among people who have limited sources of amusement, will aid in checking unkindness. The practical application of the golden rule will keep the children on the kindly side of fun.

A deep moral impression may be made by reference to each seed producing its kind, and then asking what kinds of action and feeling grow where children act and feel unkindly or rudely.]

BABY CALLA.

BABY CALLA has been put into her little bed by the kind gardener.

It was not a clean white bed with pretty hangings, in which she lay.

There were no great, fluffy pillows for her golden head to nestle against. The sheets that covered her were brown and damp, and the place was very dark.

When the man made up the bed for the little baby, he took great pains to have it smooth and nice. He patted it gently with his trowel, and left the blankets off all day, that the sun might warm it.

Then he laid the little baby in very carefully, and covered her over with the brown blankets. He did not allow even the tip of her nose to show above them.

Baby Calla did not want to be covered up. But the wise old gardener knew what was best for such little tots, and he packed her snugly in.

"Oh, how cruel to make me lie here in this dark place!" cried the little one. "It was bad enough, I am sure, in the box, but this damp, musty bed is a thousand times more dreadful!"

Then she lay quite still, thinking.

"I wonder how long I am to stay here!" she cried, after trying in vain to drop off to sleep.

Then she tried to throw off the blankets, but they were so heavy she could not lift them.

"Oh dear, oh dear! How very tiresome it is, to be sure! If I were only a little bigger, I would not be many minutes in getting these dirty old bedquilts off my poor head. How I do wish that I could grow!"

Just then a clear, soft light from a pretty lantern lit up the place where she lay, and something cool touched her face.

"Wait," said a queer little voice beside her, — "wait, and you shall grow."

"How do you know that?" asked Baby Calla, gazing in wonder at the handsome lamp which the stranger carried.

Calla Lily.
From *Das Pflanzenreich* (The Plant Kingdom), 1900.

"Oh," was the reply, "I have seen hundreds of nice babies, just like you, put in the beds and covered up. They always come up beautifully."

"How do they get out?" asked Baby Calla.

"Well, they grow — and grow — and grow, until they are quite large enough and strong enough to throw off the covers and look out. You will be very beautiful by and by if you wait."

"My good friend, you seem to know everything," said the Baby Calla. "Perhaps you will tell me your name."

"Indeed I will! It is Glowworm."

"That is a pretty name. Do you always carry a lamp with you?"

"Yes, always. But it burns brightest in damp places. Now I must be going. Good by."

Sometimes a small army of tiny creatures would tramp past her, but it was too dark for her to see them.

Soon she found a new, strange feeling swelling within her bosom. Then a voice said, "Arise, my child, for it is morning!"

And as she lifted her head above the brown coverlet, lo! the plain wrapper she had worn so long unclasped itself from about her neck, and slipped off.

Then she was in the light again. "Oh, how lovely it is!" she said.

She looked about her and saw so many things that she quite forgot herself. But when she remembered to look, she stood bathed in the beautiful sunlight, robed in the finest green satin, with diamonds on her bosom.

And she grew, and grew, fairer and fairer, taller and more stately, until the dear little glowworm's light could no longer shine upon her face.

Then the gardener came one day, and with his trowel lifted her and placed her in a lovely vessel of gold and silver. After this she was carried to the palace of the good little Princess Lightheart.

And the dear Princess Lightheart called her Calla Lily.

From STICKNEY'S READER.

SECOND WEEK OF APRIL.

THE birds that went to the warm country last autumn are coming back to us. The trees will soon be covered with green leaves, and the birds will be flying about with straws and feathers in their beaks. Last September we heard a story about a bramble bush which we will hear again this week.

THE WIND AND THE SUN.

The North Wind and the Sun once fell into a dispute as to which was the stronger of the two. They related their famous exploits, and each ended as he began, by thinking he had the greater power.

Just then a traveller came in sight, and they agreed to test the matter by trying to see which of them could soonest get off the cloak he wore wrapped around him. The boastful North Wind was the first to try.

He blew a most furious blast, and nearly tore the cloak from its fastenings at his first attempt; but the man only held his cloak the more closely, and old Boreas spent his strength in vain. Mortified by his failure to do so simple a thing, he at last withdrew.

The North Wind and the Sun.
From *The Æsop for Children with Pictures by Milo Winter.*

Then came the kindly Sun, dispelling the clouds that had gathered, and sending his warmest rays straight down upon the traveller's head. Growing faint with sudden heat, the man quickly flung aside his cloak, and hastened for protection to the nearest shade.

You may guess if you can who made that story.

[When the children have guessed "Æsop," let them give a little sketch of him if any of them remember about him, and if they cannot recall anything, the teacher may repeat. A reference to the cabinet with the clay mouse and lion, or hare and tortoise, will aid the memory.]

THIRD WEEK OF APRIL.

YOU will learn, if you watch the birds, that they do not all build their nests in the same way. Some people like brick houses and some like houses of wood; some like cottages and some prefer houses that look like churches; the birds have their own tastes and fashions of building, so that the people who have studied their habits can tell at once what kind of bird built any nest you may show them. Even a small child will soon learn to know an oriole's nest from that of a robin, and a yellow-bird's nest from that of a swallow.

[Every teacher must have some personal observation of nest–building to tell the children, which will possess greater interest for them than any story from books.]

A Queer Place for a Bird's Home.
From *A Third Reader* by Jenny H. Stickney, 1889.

A QUEER PLACE FOR A BIRD'S HOME.

One evening a poor man, who had travelled many miles, lay down on the leaves in a pleasant wood to sleep. Before he went to sleep he pulled off one shoe, for it had chafed his foot and made it very sore. In the morning when he tried to put on his shoe, it hurt his foot so badly that he groaned aloud. He gave up trying to wear it, and threw it into the bushes.

The shoe caught in the fork of a young maple-tree, and hung fast by the heel, with the toe downward. The poor man limped away on his journey, and went I don't know where.

Before many days a bright–eyed little bird spied the shoe. She thought it would be a fine place to build a home in. So she and her mate brought fine twigs and straw and leaves in their bills. They placed them in the shoe in pretty nest–shape, and lined their new house with soft hair and wool.

Beth and her papa were out searching the woods for wild flowers one day. The shadow of the shoe fell on the moss beneath the little maple.

Looking up, Beth saw the nest. Her papa bent the maple down, and Beth looked in. She saw five cunning little blue eggs lying cosily against the gray lining.

Beth is a tiny girl, just passed being rocked to sleep in mamma's lap. She laughed aloud, and clapped her fat little hands for joy, when she saw this dainty sight.

"There will be birds here before long," said her papa, "and you shall come to see them."

From STICKNEY'S READER.

Frederic Froebel.

1897.

FOURTH WEEK OF APRIL.

CAN you name any of the great and good people of whom you have heard this year?

The kindergartens in Germany and America are going to celebrate a birthday this month, the birthday of the best friend the children have had since the Christ Child came to the earth.

The name of this friend is Frederic Froebel.

[Tell the story of Froebel's life].

FIFTH WEEK OF APRIL.

WE have no more snowstorms now, but instead we have "April showers," which the children often say "bring May-flowers."

How do you think the water gets up into the clouds?

[Be sure to get the children's notions before giving them the facts.]

[Sprinkle the floor, being sure that the floor is clean, or the experiment will fail. When the water has evaporated, ask the children where it has gone. If the floor is too dusty for this experiment, a clean handkerchief may be saturated with water and hung in the sun to dry. Get the children's ideas of what has become of the water when the handkerchief is dry. Tell them of the constant evaporation from the seas, lakes, and rivers.]

THE DROP OF WATER.

[Get the children to guess on authorship.]

You know, surely, what the microscope is — that wonderful little glass which makes everything appear a hundred times larger than it really is.

If you look at a single drop of ditch water through a microscope, you will see a thousand odd-looking creatures, such as you never could imagine dwelling in water. The appearance is not unlike that of

From *The Microscope: Its History, Construction, and Application,*
Being a Familiar Introduction to the Use of the Instrument
and the Study of Microscopical Science by Jabez Hogg, 1861.

a whole plateful of shrimps, all jumping and crowding upon each other; and yet, after their fashion, they are merry and happy.

Now, there was once an old man, whom his neighbors called Cribbley Crabbley — a curious name, to be sure: it meant something like creep-and-crawl. He always liked to make the most of everything, and when he could not manage it fairly, he tried magic.

One day he sat looking through his microscope, or magnifying–glass, at a drop of water brought from a neighboring ditch. What a scene of scrambling and swarming it was, to be sure! All the thousands of little creatures in the water jumped and sprang about.

"Upon my word, this is really shocking; there must surely be some way to make them live in peace and quiet, so that each attends only to his own concerns." And he thought and thought, but still could not hit upon any expedient. So he must needs have recourse to conjuring.

"I must give them color, so that they may be seen more plainly," said he; and accordingly he poured something that looked like a drop of red wine upon the drop of water. And now all the strange little creatures immediately became red all over, and looked for all the world like a whole town full of Indians.

"Why, what have you here?" asked another old magician, who had no name at all, which made him even more remarkable than Cribbley Crabbley.

"If you can find out what it is," replied Cribbley Crabbley, "I will give it to you; but I'll warn you you'll not do so easily."

And now the conjurer without a name looked through the microscope. It really seemed to him that the scene before him was a whole town, where the people ran about in the wildest way.

Those that were under wanted to be at the top, while those that chanced to be at the top must needs thrust themselves underneath; the way they struggled and kicked and bumped their heads was quite shocking.

"This is uncommonly droll and amusing!" said the nameless magician.

"Do you think so? but what do you think it is?" asked Cribbley Crabbley. "Can you find it out?"

"It is easy enough to guess, to be sure," was the reply of the nameless magician; "easy enough. It is either Paris or Copenhagen or some other large city. I don't know which, for they are all alike. It is some large city, of course."

"It is a drop of water from a puddle," said Cribbley Crabbley.

ANDERSEN.

A view of countryside with farm buildings along roadway in New Jersey.
Jacob Hoffman, 1794.

FIRST WEEK OF MAY.

WHAT is happening out in the fields? Millions of little roots are creeping downward, and millions of little stems are climbing upward. The earth is often called "Good Mother" because it nourishes so many plants. Good Mother Earth has held all the little sleeping seeds and roots during the winter, and now she is feeding them as they awake from their sleep.

[A Legend of the Cowslip may be told, What are the Dandelions? or Iddly Bung's April Christmas-Tree. The latter to be told whenever horse-chestnut-trees are in bloom. If the story of Flax is to be told, a pennyworth of flax seed may be sown, or each child provided with a tiny flower-pot in which three or four flax

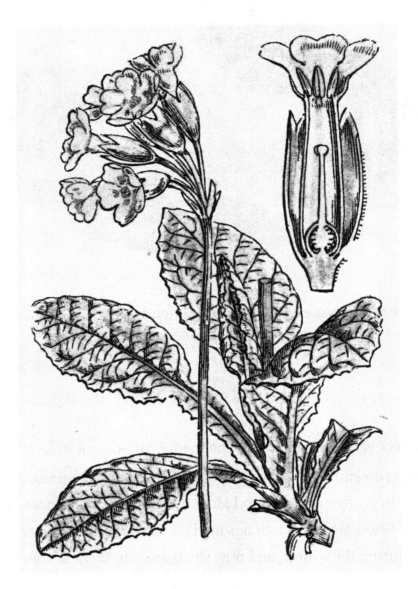

Cowslip - Primula veris.

From *Illustrations of the British Flora*, 1924.

seeds may be placed, so that the fair blue blossom, "delicate as the moth's wing," may be observed by the children at a later period.]

A LEGEND OF THE COWSLIP.

There was a time, long ago, when the Cowslip had no golden blossoms. To be sure, she wished to have them, but as she did not know how to bloom, she contented herself, for one summer, with her rich, dark leaves, and in autumn fell asleep with her feet curled close and warm under ground, and her head tucked beneath the cover which her mother had provided.

But one night she woke with a little shiver, and said, —

"Mother, I'm cold;" and her mother hastened to cover her with a gayly colored blanket of leaves, after which she slept many days and nights, until a frosty, starry hour came, when she stirred a little, and whispered, —

"Mother, I'm cold."

Then her mother covered her with a white blanket, soft as down upon the mother-bird's breast, and our Cowslip slept softly but soundly many weeks.

One May morning she heard a delightful rustling all around her, whereupon she nestled in her bed, not knowing that the rustle was caused by the whispering of her companions under ground, who, like her, were just awakening from happy dreams, pushing out their white feet, and stretching up their tiny hands, as you have seen waking babies do.

Then she heard a robin sing; but as the earth still covered her, the song was but half-understood, and to hear better, she lifted her head high enough for a yellow sunbeam, who had been looking everywhere for her, to see her.

She remembered both the sunbeam and the robin, and so glad was she to see them both, that she laughed a low, sweet "Ha, ha, ha, ha!" and there she stood in full bloom, every ha, ha! having become a smiling, sunny-hearted blossom.

Of course she was amazed, and hung her head in a sweetly modest fashion, as do cowslips to this day; for since that happy spring-time, not one of the family has forgotten to laugh itself into golden bloom, when it hears the robin and sees the yellow sunbeam of merry May.

WHAT ARE THE DANDELIONS?

"Mamma, what are the dandelions?" asked little Susy, as she saw them for the first time in her life, which you must know had not been very long.

"They are flowers, Susy."

"I know that, mamma; but they are something more than — than —" but Susy could think of no flower which was only a flower to her; so she asked another question.

"Do their roots go down, down, very deep, mamma?"

"Deeper than the roots of most small flowers; but why do you ask that, Susy?"

"Oh, I thought they must go down to the gold, and draw it up into the sunshine; that would make the gold happy, and that is the reason the dandelions laugh."

Taraxacum officinale Web.

Common Dandelion.

From *Kohler's Medizinal Pflanzen*

In Naturgetreuen Abbildungen Mit Kurz Erläuterndem Texte

(Kohler's Medicinal Plant in Lifelike Images with Short Texts), 1887.

Susy walked on without speaking again, until she and her mamma reached one of the pleasant parlors on Beacon Street, which overlooks the Common, and then she clapped her hands, and cried, —

"I see it, I see it now! Mamma, why didn't you tell me it was God's spatter-work?"

"I did not think of that," answered her mamma.

"What did you think?"

"Nothing so beautiful as your thought, my child; but I will tell you. I thought of the beautiful myth of Freya, in whom the Goths believed. They tell that she was forsaken by her husband, and, in her grief, wandered all over the earth shedding golden tears."

"And the dandelions grew up where her golden tears fell, didn't they, mamma?"

"Perhaps they did; for the Goths tell that before her there was winter, but as soon as she passed, flowers sprang up, until the whole earth blossomed."

IDDLY BUNG'S APRIL CHRISTMAS-TREE.

Of course his real name was not Iddly Bung; but that was what he called himself when he tried to say "Little Ben," in answer to the oft-repeated question, "What is your name, little man?" For no one passed the house in the outskirts of a Georgian city without noticing the great-eyed, small-bodied child who carried bundles of sticks, or buckets of water — the latter making him look like some strange animal with one broad ear standing upright; for the bucket was not a bucket, neither was it a pail, but a piggin which he carried on his head. If you were to tell Ben that a piggin is a wooden dipper, Ben would laugh at you, and ask if folks didn't milk into piggins. If you said they did, he would say, "Well, folks don't milk into dippers, do they?"

Ben was a poor boy who tried to do all he could for his mother, who went out to sew. As he was alone most of the time, he did not learn to talk plainly, as boys do who play much with other children.

In the morning he would creep quietly out of bed, look lovingly at his mother, wishing it would not waken her to "love" her just a little. Ben had never learned that there was any love but that expressed by hugging, patting, and kissing. So he would deny himself until the fire was made, and the kettle placed over it, when he would kiss his mother's eyes open; for she had let him think that they could not open until his lips unlocked them. Sometimes he would open one of them with kisses, and playfully threaten to keep the other shut all day; and there would be great glee when the eyelid was unsealed with the precious kiss.

One April day, after the trees were quite green with leaves, the mountain brooks fringed with the sweet wild jessamine, and even the laurel had hung out its waxen sprays of pink and white blossoms to tell the children it was too late to look for arbutus, Captain Jennings started on horseback to look at the mountain streams, and learn if it were true that there was danger of a flood. Sometimes the lovely valley land in Georgia is overflowed suddenly; for the snow high up in the mountains melts, and rushes down to the rivers faster than the rivers can run to the ocean. Then there is what they call a "backwater"; that is, the water is crowded back and spreads through the valley, covering houses and sometimes drowning people. Captain Jennings was alone, and as he galloped out into the open country, he saw a little boy riding a stick the same way in which he was going.

The child looked so much like his little sister of thirty years ago, that he stopped and asked him his name, and how he would like to trade horses. The boy was Ben; and, looking wishfully at the gay horse and handsome rider, thinking that he had never been on a real horse, and remembering what his mother had told him about the Good Friend who never made fun of people, he said boldly, with tears flashing in his great eyes, "I fought you was Dod; but he wouldn't make fun of me and my sossy" (horse). Captain Jennings felt sad, for he did not mean to make fun of Ben; and, thinking of the little sister, whose eyes used so easily to fill with tears, he said kindly, "I did not mean to make fun of you, my boy. Will you ride with me on this horse?" "When will you bing me bat?" "Before sundown; jump up, little one." And Ben was on a live, prancing horse instead of a stick.

They rode through thickets of oak, and Ben stripped the leaves as they flew past, and flung them to the wind, which seemed to him to meet them everywhere, just to catch his leaves and toss his hair. They scared up partridges, that whirred about with much ado, and sat down again while Ben was still in sight. What wonderland was this to little Ben, who had never before been three miles from home!

At last Ben saw something which made him cry softly, "Please stop; there is Dod's own, own Trismas-tree!" Captain Jennings stopped his horse and looked; there stood a tree, forty feet high, with long leaves that looked like emerald jewels, with fretted edges, and tapers that held within them such soft, mellow light as never waxen

Balsam Fir.
P. Freeman Heim. Provided by National Agricultural Library.

tapers dreamed of shedding. Captain Jennings took off his hat, while Ben asked if they could not wait for the angels who lighted the candles to come back. You do not believe they saw any such thing? If you never saw a horse-chestnut-tree in bloom, you may well think this an untrue story; but if you have seen one, you will not wonder that little Ben thought it "Dod's own, own Trismas-tree." Ben asked Captain Jennings if he thought the angels would care if he took a branch with just two candles to his mother. What a happy boy was he when he had the branch in his hand! He hugged it to his breast, and kissed the candle, which he was sure the angels had but just touched.

Captain Jennings had made up his mind that there was great danger of a flood, and he galloped home so fast that Ben could not catch a leaf of the trees that brushed his face as they hurried onward. They were soon at Ben's door, and Captain Jennings dropped Ben quickly to the ground, and spurred his horse to a gallop, — thinking, as he did so, that this house of Ben's stood on low ground, but soon forgetting it in anxious work for the safety of the town.

After working until late in the evening, Captain Jennings went to bed, leaving a boat chained to his window, and was soon asleep. Later in the night he was awakened by the steady, heavy patter, patter, patter, of rain upon his windows. He rose and looked out; there was darkness, and cloud, and chilling rain above; and below, the black water was creeping softly and darkly all around his house.

There was no light where the stars sometimes shine, but far out on the water he saw red lights from scores of little boats that were gliding here and there, taking people to the hills, from houses that were fast filling with water.

Captain Jennings did not want to go into all that cold and dark which was outside his door. He had moved up stairs, so he did not mind if the first floor of his house was filled with water. Why should he not go to bed and to sleep? It is not pleasant to row in a heavy rain, to dodge floating houses, and hear the cries of frightened children; so he would go to bed. But as his head sank into the warm pillow, he thought of little Ben and "Dod's own, own Trismas-tree"; of the low ground on which Ben's house stood; the loneliness of the place; the feelings which people must have who have no boat at such a time; of the lost sister of whom Ben had made him think all day; of that dark water, crawling with its soft plash higher, higher, higher, until — what if Ben and his "Trismas-tree" were left entirely to the angels!

Who knows but the angels were thus calling to Captain Jennings to help them?

Be that as it may, Captain Jennings was out in his boat by the time he had thought all this, and was rowing swiftly towards the little house, thinking of little Ben, the little "Trismas-tree," and the far-away little sister, who must be a woman now.

As he came near the house, he heard a glad cry from Ben, who had seen the lantern coming that way. Ben and his mother were out on the house-roof, the water having nearly reached the eaves. But Ben, with the faith of a child and the courage of a man, was assuring his mother that help would come before they floated away. For "of tourse Dod watched his Trismas-tree," and must see Ben, who had a branch of it in his wee hand, really thinking more of the angels who lighted the candles than of any present danger.

Of course they were taken from the roof to the boat; and carried to a place of safety.

Ben thinks "Dod's Trismas-tree" saved their lives. Ben's mother thinks that it would have been from no forgetfulness or unkindness of their Heavenly Father if their lives had been lost. And Captain Jennings would like to know just how much the angels had to do with that flood, and the April Christmas-tree, and the finding of his darling sister, whom Ben's mother proved to be.

THE FLAX.

The flax was in full bloom; it had pretty little blue flowers as delicate as the wings of a moth, or even more so. The sun shone, and the showers watered it; and this was as good for the flax as it is for little children to be washed and then kissed by their mothers. They look much prettier for it, and so did the flax.

"People say that I look exceedingly well," said the flax, "and that I am so fine and long that I shall make a beautiful piece of linen. How fortunate I am! It makes me so happy, it is such a pleasant thing to know that something can be made of me. How the sunshine cheers me, and how sweet and refreshing is the rain! My happiness overpowers me; no one in the world can feel happier than I.

"Tomorrow the sun will shine, or the rain descend. I feel that I am growing. I feel that I am in full blossom. I am the happiest of all creatures."

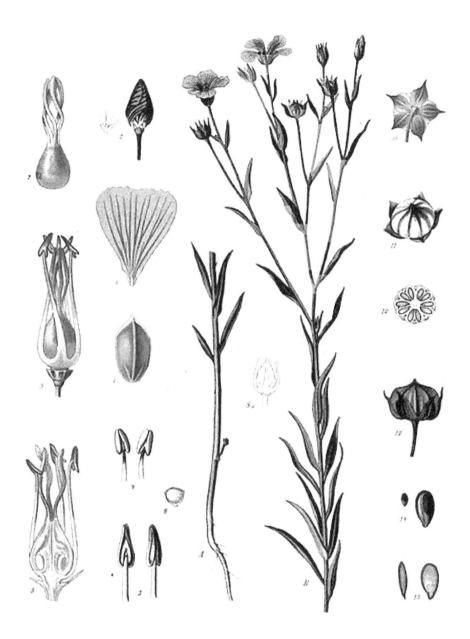

Linum Usitatissimum — Flax.
From *Kohler's Medizinal Pflanzen*
In Naturgetreuen Abbildungen Mit Kurz Erläuterndem Texte
(Kohler's Medicinal Plant in Lifelike Images with Short Texts), 1887.

One day some people came, who took hold of the flax and pulled it up by the roots. Then it was laid in water, as if they intended to drown it; and after that, placed near a fire as if it were to be roasted.

"We cannot expect to be happy always," said the flax.

It was steeped, and roasted, and broken, and combed; indeed, it scarcely knew what was done to it. At last it was put on the spinning-wheel. "Whirr, whirr," went the wheel, so quickly that the flax could not collect its thoughts.

"Well, I have been very happy," he thought, "and I must be contented with the past;" and contented he remained till he was put on the loom, and became a beautiful piece of white linen. All the flax, even to the last stalk, was used in making this one piece. "Well, this is quite wonderful. I could not have believed that I should be so favored by fortune. How wonderful it is that, after all I have suffered, I am made something of at last. I am the luckiest person in the world, — so strong and fine; and how white, and what a length! This is something different from being a mere plant and bearing flowers. Then, I had no attention, nor any water unless it rained; now, I am watched and taken care of. Every morning the maid turns me over, and I have a shower-bath from the watering-pot every evening. Yes, and the clergyman's wife noticed me, and said I was the best piece of linen in the whole parish. I cannot be happier than I am now."

After some time the linen was taken into the house, placed under the scissors, and cut and torn into pieces, and then pricked with needles. This certainly was not pleasant; but at last it was made into little dresses for babies!

"See now, then," said the flax; "I have become something of importance. This was my destiny; it is quite a blessing. Now I shall be of some use in the world, as every one ought to be; it is the only way to be happy."

Years passed away; and at last the linen was so worn that the little dresses fell to pieces. "It must end very soon," said the sleeves to each other. "We would gladly have held together a little longer, but it is useless to expect impossibilities." And at length they fell into rags and tatters, and thought it was all over with them, for they were torn into shreds, and steeped in water, and ground into a pulp, and dried, and they knew not what besides; till all at once they found themselves beautiful white paper. "Well, now, this is a surprise; a glorious surprise, too," said the paper. "I am now finer than ever, and I shall be written upon, and who can tell what fine things I may have written upon me. This is wonderful luck!" And sure enough the most beautiful stories and poetry were written upon it, and only once was there a blot, which was very fortunate. Then people heard the stories and poetry read, and it made them wiser and better; for all that was written had a good and sensible meaning, and a great blessing was contained in the words on this paper.

"I never imagined anything like this," said the paper, "when I was only a little blue flower, growing in the fields. How could I fancy that I should ever be the means of bringing joy to men? I cannot understand it myself, and yet it is really so. Heaven knows that I have done nothing myself, but what I was obliged to do with my weak powers for my own preservation; and yet I have been promoted from one joy and honor to another. Each time I think that the song is ended, and then something higher and better begins for me. I suppose now I shall be sent on my travels about the world, so that people may read me. It cannot be otherwise; indeed, it is more than probable, for I have more splendid thoughts written upon me than I had pretty flowers in olden times. I am happier than ever."

But the paper did not go on its travels. It was sent to the printer, and all the words written upon it were set up in type to make a book, or rather many hundreds of books, for so many more persons could derive pleasure and profit from a printed book than from the written paper; and if the paper had been sent about the world, it would have been worn out before it had got half through its journey.

"This is certainly the wisest plan," said the written paper. "I really did not think of that. I shall remain at home, and be held in honor like some old grandfather, as I really am to these new books. They will do some good. I could not have wandered about as they do. Yet he who wrote all this has looked at me as every word flowed from his pen upon my surface. I am the most honored of all."

Then the paper was tied in a bundle with other papers, and thrown into a tub that stood in the wash-house.

"After work, it is well to rest," said the paper, "and a very good opportunity to collect one's thoughts. Now I am able, for the first time, to think of my real condition; and to know one's self is true progress. What will be done with me now, I wonder? No doubt I shall still go forward. I have always progressed hitherto, as I know quite well."

Now it happened one day that all the paper in the tub was taken out and laid on the hearth to be burnt. People said it could not be sold at the shop, to wrap up butter and sugar, because it had been written upon. The children in the house stood round the stove, for they wanted to see the paper burn, because it flamed up so prettily, and afterwards, among the ashes, so many red sparks could be seen running one after the other, here and there, as quick as the wind. They called it seeing the children come out of school, and the last spark was the schoolmaster. They often thought the last spark had come, and one would cry, "There goes the schoolmaster!" but the next moment another spark would appear, shining so beautifully. How they would like to know where the sparks all went to! Perhaps we shall find out some day, but we don't know now.

The whole bundle of paper had been placed on the fire; and was soon alight. "Ugh!" cried the paper, as it burst into a bright flame; "ugh!"

It was certainly not very pleasant to be burning; but when the whole was wrapped in flames, the flames mounted up into the air, higher than the flax had ever been able to raise its little blue flower, and they glistened as the white linen never could have glistened. All the written letters became quite red in a moment, and all the words and thoughts turned to fire.

"Now I am mounting straight up to the sun," said a voice in the flames; and it was as if a thousand voices echoed the words; and the flames darted up through the chimney, and went out at the top. Then a number of tiny beings, as many in number as the flowers on the flax had been, and invisible to mortal eyes, floated above them. They were even lighter and more delicate than the flowers from which they were born; and as the flames were extinguished, and nothing remained of the paper but black ashes, these little beings danced upon it, and whenever they touched it, bright red sparks appeared.

"The children are all out of school, and the schoolmaster was the last of all," said the children. It was good fun; and they sang over the ashes, —

> "Snip, snap, snurre,
> Basse lurre,
> The song is ended."

But the little invisible beings said, "The song is never ended; the most beautiful is yet to come."

But the children could neither hear nor understand this; nor should they, for children must not know everything.

ANDERSEN.

Monarch Caterpillar,
Hung Up for Pupation, a Chrysalis, and an Adult.

SECOND WEEK OF MAY.

HAVE you ever seen any birds building their nests? Have you ever seen any birds' eggs? What kinds of eggs have you seen? The people of Norseland used to call butterflies Freya's hens.

Butterflies lay beautiful little eggs; some of them are so small that you can hardly see them, but under a magnifying-glass you can see that the eggs of various kinds of butterflies differ as much as the eggs of a robin differ from those of a pigeon.

By a little care the teacher can easily show the children the caterpillar, chrysalis, and butterfly of the Danais Archippus, or common milkweed butterfly. Look sharply on the under side of milkweed leaves where a yellow-white egg is deposited, or, if very near hatching-time, the egg will be a dull gray. The larva emerges from the egg in about a week, and seeing the tiny creature eat its own eggshell is a delight. It is better to remove the tiny caterpillar to a milkweed by the highway, as artificial conditions are too apt to bring only disappointment for the children, and full-grown larvae are easily captured which remain in chrysalis but thirteen days. The full-grown larva should be placed under a wire screen, with fresh milkweed leaves in a bottle of water. They are likely to go into the chrysalis stage after a few days, and remain a little less than two weeks, when the butterflies will appear.

The Colias, or common yellow butterfly, is also easily watched through three changes; the caterpillar is a common green one, a little more than an inch long, and is often found on clover leaves. The Cottage Place children found large numbers of them on the nasturtiums in the yard, some of which were transferred to the window-boxes and given the freedom of the house. A chrysalis attached itself to the window-pane, which we covered with plenty of mosquito-netting pasted to the sash, and one morning we had a perfect Colias, which took kindly to our fingers until its wings were

Colias edusa — Clouded Yellow Butterfly.
A History of British Butterflies, 1870.

well shaken out, when it was agreed he should fly where he pleased; he pleased to stay in our windows a day or two, when he soared away.

One such study of a butterfly will quench the desire to crush them under hats more effectually than any persuasion or commands.

[The story of The Green House with Gold Nails, or The Bees' Pockets, or Carl and The Earthworms may be told.]

THE GREEN HOUSE WITH GOLD NAILS.

Among the butterflies which flit gayly about our summer flowers, there was one in which I was much interested last season. It has been my "progressive object card" for the summer, and I do not believe even the Little School-ma'am would object to my studies when I tell her that no pin or other instrument of torture has been used, either in its capture or mounting.

How did I catch my butterfly? As I would advise all to do who wish for success and a perfect specimen. Take with you a box; watch for a nice plump caterpillar; break off the leaf you will easily find him feeding upon; and when you have carried him home in the box put him on a white paper and invert a clear plain-glass tumbler quickly over him; feed him daily with whatever sort of leaf you found him eating, and you have caught your butterfly. You can see him through the glass, and will find it a source of enjoyment to watch from time to time his great changes.[*]

But it is of one particular kind I wish now to tell you. The caterpillar lives upon the common milkweed which grows by the roadside, with pinkish clusters of flowers in summer, and curious bird-shaped pods in the fall. This caterpillar is very pretty, and the butterfly is handsome; but the crowning beauty of all is the chrysalis. It looks like a little green house, put together with gold nails. It is somewhat of the size and shape of a long, delicate pea-green acorn, and has a row of dots half-way around what would be the saucer of the acorn, with others about the size of a pin's head on different parts

---

[*] [A wire screen is better than the glass for obvious reasons.]

Plate from *Metamorphosis of a Butterfly*.
By Merian Maria Sybilla, 1705.

of the chrysalis, and you will say they are not *like* gold, but are real gold itself.

The caterpillar, when full grown, is about two inches long. It is cylindrical, and handsomely marked with narrow alternating bands of black, white, and lemon-yellow. The bands are not entirely even, and occasionally run into each other. On the top of the second ring or segment are two slender, black, thread-like horns, and on a hind ring two more, not quite as long as those near the head. You can find it almost any day in July or August, if you look closely on the under side of the broad leaves of the milkweed. It was the accidental finding of his chrysalis, attached to a spray of wild carrot, that led me to study this particular species. It was a secret to me — this beautiful green and gold house. It held something. What, I must know! Cutting the stem of the carrot, I brought the treasure carefully into the house, covered it with a tumbler, and for a week it remained just the same. Then the green began to turn to a light purple, and lines began to show through the clear case. The front showed lines like a curtain, parted and folded back each way like a drapery, to the bottom. The back was curiously marked off. The whole gradually took on a very dark purple hue, and I hoped to see it open and give up its treasure. But though I watched very carefully, it stole a march on me, and one morning I found its secret disclosed and fluttering below the empty chrysalis, now but a clear, rent tissue, with here and there a gold dot. The butterfly is handsome and quite large (more than three inches across when the wings are spread), but not quite so beautiful as you would infer from his elegant house. He is of a rich, tawny orange, bordered with velvety black on the upper side, and a lighter nankeen yellow below, and has a large velvety black head spotted with white.

Learning that he came from the milkweed caterpillar, I went in quest of some. I was fortunate enough to find five. I put them in a glass fernery about one foot long and ten inches high, and fed them with fresh milkweed leaves daily. Soon they mounted, one after another, to the top, and began to work on the under side of the glass cover. My curiosity was on the alert to see how each would build his green house. I had seen cocoons of various kinds spun, but the glass-smooth chrysalis could not be spun. Oh, no! It was altogether too nice work to be done in sight. There was no sound of hammer or sight of tools. It was all polished and painted and ready — and lo! the inner layers of the caterpillar's skin had been the workshop, and the outer skin was taken down and discarded, like worthless scaffolding, when the green and gold house was ready. Pretty soon there were five of these houses hanging from the glass roof, side by side; and now there are five empty homes, still clinging by the little shiny black twist that fastens them firmly to the glass, and five handsome butterflies. Only one of all these did I see break the shell. The butterfly was packed, head downward, at the bottom of the chrysalis — wonderfully packed, as all will admit who see him emerge, to shake himself out into something five or six times as wide, a beautiful uncramped butterfly.

Mrs. Julia P. Ballard, in *Insect Lives, or Born in a Prison.*

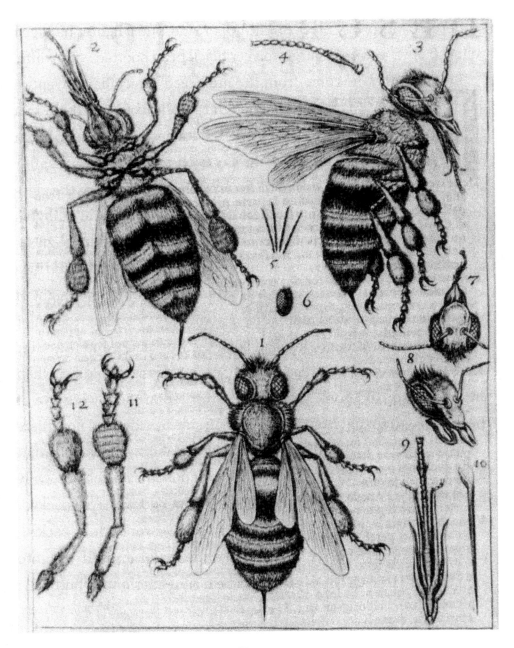

Bees.
The oldest known drawing that was made with a microscope.
Francesco Stelluti, 1630.

THE BEES' POCKETS.

Bees are very curious little creatures. I suppose they are the most useful of all the insects that fly. They are only about an inch long, and yet what wonderful work they do, all summer long, making so much honey and wax for us!

They know, too, about every flower in our gardens, and all the signs of the weather; and then they are so kind to their children. When they make their honey, I wonder if you know how they get their materials. Let me tell you.

Bees have slender-pointed hairs upon their heads. The yellow hairs upon their legs, which we can see with the naked eye, turn out to be a hard, horny sort of comb which they use in the gathering and storing of the pollen of flowers.

Besides this, the bees have two little baskets upon their thighs which are the very nicest of side-pockets, just such as we should want for holding things.

But what do you think they do with these pockets? They first tuck their little heads into the heart of the rose or lily, or other sweet flower, for honey. In doing so they cover them all over with the yellow dust, which is the pollen.

Then they take their fore-feet and brush it very carefully from the hair, and pass it on to the middle feet, and on again to the hind-feet, where it is safely packed in these little pockets on the thighs. As soon as they are loaded, they fly away home and put it in some secret place. Some of the pollen is given to their babies, and some of it is worked up into wax. This, you know is made into cells.

The bees are so industrious, that in five days, by the use of these pockets, they can half fill the hive with honey-comb. The honey-comb makes wax, and the wax is used in a great many ways. When you look at your most beautiful dolls, don't forget that they are really made by the bees, or at least that the wax for their faces is. You can learn a great deal about bees by carefully watching them about their hives or among the flowers.

From STICKNEY'S READER.

CARL AND THE EARTHWORMS.

Carl's hands were dirty; Carl's face was dirty; Carl's finger-nails were black at the ends; Carl's clothes were soiled; Carl's hair was not brushed, and his head looked like an old chestnut burr.

Carl could not tell if he had ever had a bath, and I do not believe that he had had more than three in the three years in which he had been able to walk alone. But when Carl went to the kindergarten, a gentlewoman took off his soiled clothes, put him in a tub of clean water, and with brush, soap, and towels, made him look almost like a cherub. When he was dressed in fresh clean clothes, he felt as if he could never be dirty again; and he was so happy that when he went out to play, he wanted to make everybody and everything happy too. In the garden he found an earthworm, and by digging, he found as many as he had fingers; and he ran for a wash-basin and some warm water, and before the gentlewoman knew what he was doing, he had them all washed, and was vainly trying to hang them on the fence to dry; for, said he, "Poor dirty things! they want to be clean for once in their lives." But they did not want to hang on the fence, and they did want to get back into the cool dark earth. When he understood that that would make them happy, he put them back, and heard, with great surprise, that they had much work to do underground, ploughing and boring the whole earth, making it soft and loose about the little seeds, so they can grow; the earth needing as many of these little living ploughs as there are seeds.

Now when Carl digs up an earthworm, he puts him back in great haste, saying, "Go back to your work, little earthworm; you are good to my flower-seeds, and I will be good to you."

THIRD WEEK OF MAY.

THE children of our family all have the same family name, but each has a name beside. There may be Harry Rowe, Fred Rowe, Nellie Rowe, and Mary Rowe, the last name showing to what family each child belongs. It is so among butterflies and flowers.

There are a great many flowers, for instance, that belong to the Rose family, and many others that belong to the Lily family.

Most children know roses from lilies as soon as they see them; but there are some belonging to each family not so easily known.

[A little help from the teacher will enable the children to recognize the most common representatives of the two families. The value of this is not, of course, in the bit of botanical knowledge, but in the suggestion to the children of the fields of delightful study opening before them.]

OAK-TREE AND ACORN.

HELPS TO AN OBJECT LESSON.

Just as there are many children here with different names, so in the woods there are many trees, each having its own name. And as there are brothers and sisters among children, so there are relations among trees. This acorn which you see came from an oak-tree, whose first name is "Red." All the farmers, and woodmen, and sawyers, and

White Oak.
P. Freeman Heim. Provided by National Agricultural Library.

ship-builders know him as Red Oak. He has brothers called Swamp Oak, Willow Oak, White Oak, etc.

The oak-tree is very useful, for its wood is so hard and firm that it is used for building ships that must be strong enough not to split open when great iron nails and spikes are driven through them. The farmers use oak-trees to make into fences, because the wood will stand out in the rain and snow a great many years without spoiling. The wood of the oak-tree does not burn easily, so it is never used for kindling fires.

Let us look at these acorns now. If we were to plant them in the ground, it would take nearly a hundred years for a large tree to grow from one of them.

The acorn is the nut of the oak-tree; but it is not good for children to eat; the pigs like acorns very much. If you look very sharply on this stem, you will see some baby acorns; they were flowers last summer, and next summer they would have been large acorns if they had been left on the tree. The oak-leaf is so different from all other leaves that I think you will know it wherever you may see it. I will draw some oak-leaves, and you may color them with your brush and paint; and you may make some acorns with the clay. Some very careful child could make a stem, leaf, and bunch of acorns that would look very much like one picked from the tree.

White Oak Acorn.
W.D. Brush. Provided by National Agricultural Library.

[The acorn is easily modelled in clay, even by the beginners.]

[Andersen's story of the Greenies may be told, the children again allowed to guess concerning the authorship. Saint Elizabeth and the Roses may be told, if preferable. The object lesson on the Oak-Tree and Acorn may be given.]

THE GREENIES.

A rose-tree stood in the window. But a little while ago it had been green and fresh, and now it looked sickly, — it was in poor health, no doubt. A whole regiment was quartered on it, and was eating it up; yet, notwithstanding this seeming greediness, the regiment was a very decent and respectable one. It wore bright green uniforms. I spoke to one of the "Greenies"; he was but three days old, and yet he was already a grandfather. What do you think he said? It is all true, — he spoke of himself and of the rest of the regiment. Listen!

We are the most wonderful creatures in the world. The wisest of the creatures, the ant (we have the greatest respect for him!) understands us well. He does not eat us up; he takes our eggs, lays them in the family ant-hill on the ground floor, — lays them, labelled and numbered, side by side, layer on layer, so that each day a new one may creep out of the egg. Then he puts us in a stable, strokes our hind legs, and milks us. He has given us the prettiest of names, — "Little milch-cow."

All creatures, who, like the ant, are gifted with common sense, call us by this pretty name.

I was born on a rose-leaf. I and all the regiment live on the rose-tree. The gardener calls us plant-lice; the books call us Aphides; but the little children call us the ant's cows.

ANDERSEN.

SAINT ELIZABETH AND THE ROSES.

Saint Elizabeth daily visited the poor who dwelt in the suburbs of Eisenach, and in the huts of the neighboring valleys. One day during a severe winter, she left her castle with a single attendant, carrying in the skirts of her robe a supply of bread, meat, and eggs for a certain poor family; and as she was descending the frozen and slippery path her husband met her. Now her husband did not like to have her going out in such cold weather, and he asked her, —

"What dost thou here, my Elizabeth? let us see what heavy burden thou art carrying." And she, confused and blushing to be so discovered, pressed her mantle to her bosom; but her husband insisted, and, opening her robe, he beheld only red and white roses, more beautiful and fragrant than any that grew on earth even in summer, and it was now the depths of winter.

Then he bade her go on her way and fulfill her mission of feeding the hungry; but taking one of the roses of Paradise, he put it in his bosom and continued to ascend the mountain, thinking of the goodness of Elizabeth's heart and the greatness of Him who could change bread into roses.

FOURTH WEEK OF MAY.

YOU have seen caterpillars of various kinds, and have learned that all caterpillars go to sleep creeping creatures and wake up with wings. But all creeping things are not caterpillars; some are only worms, such as Carl found in the ground, and no one, not even Sir John Lubbock, has discovered that a worm ever becomes anything but a worm. You ought to hear about Sir John Lubbock, who lives in England, and knows more about earthworms, and ants, and bees, and wasps, perhaps, than any other man in the world.

He has studied them all a great many years, and if you should ask him if he knows all about them, what do you suppose he would say? No doubt he would answer, "I could not find out all I want to know of them if I could study them a hundred years."

[The story of The Mice in the Robin's Nest or The Harvest Mouse may be told. Object lesson on hickory-tree may be given.]

Shellbark Hickory.
W.J. Beal. Provided by National Agricultural Library.

HELPS TO AN OBJECT LESSON ON THE HICKORY-TREE.

Showing the children a shelled hickory-nut, draw from them that it is a nut and grows upon a tree. [Some of them will think of the acorn as soon as the hickory-nut is presented, and will reason from analogy that it grows on a tree.] This nut had two shells, as you will see when I show you the one in the box. Its name is Hickory-nut. Now on what kind of tree do you suppose it grows? I think somebody can tell its name. Yes, it grew on a hickory-tree; the meat is very good to eat, and if you listen well to what I tell you about the tree, you shall each have a nut to eat.

Hickory-nut.
USDA-NRCS Plants Database.

This tree grows out in the woods, sometimes standing close beside the oak-tree; but no farmer or woodman would make the mistake of cutting a hickory-tree for building a ship or a fence. Which tree would he cut for those purposes? The oak, to be sure. I am glad you remember so well. But how do you suppose he could tell which was the oak-tree? He could tell by the leaves in summer, and by the bark of the tree in winter. See, here is a hickory-leaf; its edge is not cut into such points as you saw on the oak-leaf, but it has tiny points which we will call teeth; you can feel them and see them, too. The wood of the hickory-tree makes beautiful hot fires, and when the farmer's wife is baking the pumpkin pies for the Thanksgiving dinner, she always asks her little boy to bring in some hickory-wood; and he goes out to the piles of wood and pulls out the hard, white sticks, with shaggy bark like this, and builds a fire that you would like to see in a cold day. Would you like to color the leaf of the hickory-tree with your brush and paint? You may do so when you can tell me surely which is the hickory-leaf and which the oak; and you may make the hickory-nut from clay if you like. Now we will have some hickory-nuts to eat.

[Crack one in the presence of the children, but have some prepared for eating.]

THE MICE IN A ROBIN'S NEST.

Did Mr. Robin, when he took his family south for the winter, advertise a "House to let" in the newspapers? Grandpa Baldwin wondered about it when he found who had moved into the robin's nest on the top of the quince-bush.

Grandpa was picking quinces when he noticed the nest. He was surprised to see something move in it.

At first he thought it was a dry leaf, blown by the wind. He kept glancing up at it, and pretty soon something moved again.

He did not think for a moment that it could be a little robin; for when quinces are ripe, all the little robins have grown up and have gone south.

Grandpa was very curious by this time. He climbed up the tree and peeped into the nest. He saw nothing there but a bunch of wool.

"How did wool get into that nest?" said Grandpa.

Then it moved again. Grandpa put his hand up carefully, and was just about to lift the wool, when out jumped an old mother mouse and ran away.

The Mice in a Robin's Nest.
From *A Third Reader* by Jenny H. Stickney, 1889.

Grandpa started so that he nearly fell out of the tree.

Then he lifted the wool and peeped into the nest. There he found six baby mice, all sleeping in the softest little bed you can imagine, with a nice wool mattress and coverlid.

As the old mother mouse had run away and left her babies, grandpa decided to carry the nest home and show it to mamma and the boys.

Such shouting as there was then! The "mites," as baby called them, cuddled closer and closer to each other, until one fell over the edge of the nest to the floor.

Then such a scrambling as there was to catch him! At last grandpa caught him. The mother mouse had a beautiful white breast and a fawn-colored back. Grandpa said she was a dear little mouse. The children thought they were all dear little mice.

There are a great many of them in the fields. Sometimes when the men are mowing, the mice run up their trousers' legs. Grandpa says he never before knew one to climb a tree and make a home for herself in a bird's nest.

From STICKNEY'S READER.

THE LITTLE HARVEST MOUSE.

Do you know about the nests the little field-mice hang for their children high up in the stalks of standing grain? They do not often trust their little ones to the open nest of a bird.

Their own nests are very carefully woven of narrow grasses. They are hollow globes not larger than the balls you use in your games, with always a baby mouse peeping out.

The Little Harvest Mouse.
From *A Third Reader* by Jenny H. Stickney, 1904.
Illustrated by J. Oliver Nugent.

They do not need much room, for this whole family in its nest would only weigh as much as a letter which one postage-stamp would carry.

They are the tiniest of all animals, at least of all that have bones.

What will they do when the grain is cut?

"We shall be grown-up mice then," they answer.

But what do they do?

Some of them dig a deep hole in the ground and line it with grass. Some stay in the summer nest, after the stalks have been cut and are carried to the barn or piled in stacks out of doors. They are nimble little fellows, well able to care for themselves. By the help of their long tail, and slender, flexible toes, they are among the best climbers in the world; and they are brave, too. Mice of one of the tribes are said to be like little bears.

They must be nimble, as their food consists of insects, especially flies, which they are very fond of. When they go in pursuit of them their aim is as sure as that of the swallow.

If you can get some one to catch a field-mouse for you, it will be a pretty pet, — a little Thumbling, with which you may amuse yourself. It will burrow and build in a cage, as well as anywhere, if you give it something to work with.

From STICKNEY'S READER.

FIRST WEEK OF JUNE.

NEXT September some of these children will go to public school. Here we have learned a little about things we see, there we will learn more and more as we grow older.

The children who will be old enough for public school next year may sit in a little circle by themselves and let us hear how much they can remember about the stories and object-lessons heard here.

We can easily see that the children who have been here every day remember the most; it will be just so in public school; the child that is there every day will learn the most.

[Each child in this little class may select its own clay models, and tell what it can about them; then they may exchange, and so test their knowledge.

The Story of the Elephant or The Story of the Camel may be told.]

Burmah: Elephant Working.

THE ELEPHANT.

Not so wonderful, perhaps, but wiser, larger, and stronger than the camel is the elephant. If we knew him well, we should think him the noblest of animals.

In India elephants are too common to be in shows, but sailors like to watch the trained animals at work in shipyards, moving timbers. Besides drawing great logs by a chain, they will lift heavy trunks of trees and carry them on their tusks, and will pile them evenly, pushing them into place with the right foot. When an elephant has dragged a log to the right spot, he will unhook the chain with the finger of his trunk. His driver sits sideways on a wooden saddle on the elephant's back, and makes signs by touching his side with his foot. The intelligent beast understands what is wanted of him.

Sometimes one is obliged to hold his head so high that he cannot see where he is going; but he moves on blindly and patiently. One day some people were landing when the tide was out and the wharf very muddy. There was a lady on board, and the captain would not allow her to soil her boots.

He called to a driver, and in a moment his elephant pushed a log down the slope, fixing it just right for a walk across the muddy space.

Those huge beasts seem proud of their strength. They do not like to do work which makes them look awkward; but they are obedient and make the best of it.

You have seen the elephant eat and drink, perhaps, picking up food and sucking up water with his long trunk. One could hardly believe the stout, strong trunk could bend around to put each mouthful of food into the mouth beneath. There is hardly a thing so strong or so delicate that the elephant cannot lift it safely.

If kindly treated, he is loving and gentle, and may be trusted. An elephant was once very fond of the baby in his master's family. The nurse would take the little one in its cradle, put it between the elephant's feet, and go away.

The great creature would watch over it, and move his trunk like a fan to keep off the flies. If baby awoke, he would rock the cradle back and forth, to get it off to sleep again.

An elephant in a circus was once in pain, and a doctor gave him some medicine which cured him. On the next day, when the circus passed the house, the elephant saw the doctor in his doorway and went to him to caress him with his trunk. Having shown his gratitude, he marched forward again with the rest.

From STICKNEY'S READER.

Dromedary and Two-Humped Camel.
From *The Student's Reference Work:*
A Cyclopaedia for Teachers, Students, and Families, Vol. 1, 1901.

THE CAMEL.

There was once brought me from London a collection of pictures of the most remarkable animals of the world.

I was young enough to think of them all as real, living creatures, and soon had my favorites among them.

The camel would never have known by the way I treated him that he had the first place, but I think I always valued him more highly than any of the others.

"You are so clumsy and awkward," I used to say to my camel; "I would much rather not be so wonderful and be a little more beautiful.

"Your back is too high and, though your neck is so long, you do not carry your head well. If only you had ears like my horse, and thin, graceful legs and feet, it would be better, even if you could not have a smooth, bright coat of hair."

Then I would fancy my favorite felt ill-used, for camels do have a sad, patient look, and I would take his part against myself.

I made my proud horse admit that he would be good for nothing in a desert. I talked for the camel, and asked the horse if he could cover his eyes without shutting out the light, and close his nostrils, also, from the fine, hot sand the air would be full of; and if he would find his small, hard hoofs and iron shoes useful in the deep, loose sand.

The horse did not mind my talk, and neither of the animals seemed to wish to grow more like the other.

There are two kinds of camels. One lives in Turkey and in some parts of China, and has two humps on its back.

The other lives in Arabia, and has but one hump.

How would you like to have a baby camel about three feet high? When the little camels are about two months old, their owner begins to train them for their work.

He makes them kneel every day for several hours. A piece of carpet covers them so that only the head and neck are seen. To prevent them from getting up, he puts heavy weights on the edges of the covering. This training goes on for four months.

Then the Arab children become their teachers and keepers. It is a pretty sight to see them, twice a day, feeding the little camels. In one hand they carry a bowl of camel's milk, and in the other a tiny switch.

After the bowls are empty, the children give the camels a touch on the legs with the switch. Down they all drop on their knees.

The education goes on week after week, and month after month, till the children and their pupils become very fond of each other.

The camel is full grown at the age of eight years. Its food is chiefly grass, or if that is not to be had, it seems equally well pleased with the nettles, thistles, or other coarse, prickly plants found in its long journeys.

From STICKNEY'S READER.

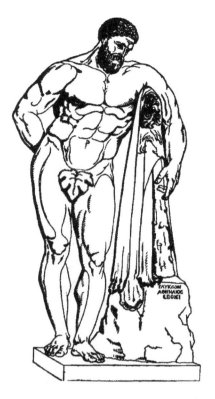

Farnese Hercules.
From *History of Ancient Art* by Franz von Reber, 1902.

SECOND WEEK OF JUNE.

As we learn to do things well we love to do them, and after doing a few things that are quite hard to do we become very fond of doing hard things. I hope these little children will always love to do hard things. There is a story about some one who wanted help to do something he could do himself if he tried. The story is what we call a fable, and was first told many hundred years ago by a man who was once a slave, but was given his freedom because he so much pleased the king with his stories. People so admired him that a statue in his honor was placed in Athens. What was his name?

[The story of The Crow and the Pitcher may be told instead, to impress a lesson of self-helpfulness and courage in overcoming difficulties.]

Hercules and the Wagoner.
From *The Children's Book* by Horace Elisha Scudder, 1881.

HERCULES AND THE WAGONER.

As a wagoner drove his wagon through a miry lane the wheels stuck fast in the clay, so that the horses could go no farther. The man, without making the least effort to remedy the matter, fell upon his knees, and began to call upon Hercules to come and help him out of his trouble.

"Lazy fellow," said Hercules, "lay your own shoulder to the wheel. Stir yourself, and do what you can. Then, if you want aid from me you shall have it. Remember the proverb,—

"'Heaven helps those that help themselves.'"

ÆSOP.

THE CROW AND THE PITCHER.

Do you know what it is to feel thirsty, so very thirsty that you can think of nothing else?

The crow thought he was ready to die of thirst.

Looking all about to find water, he spied a pitcher. "There may be water in it," he said; "I'll go and see."

He was right. There was water there, but so little that he could not reach it with his bill, though he stood on the very tips of his toes.

"Oh, dear!" he said, "what shall I do?"

The sight of it made him want it all the more.

"I could get it," he said, "if I broke the pitcher." But the pitcher was too strong for him to break.

"I might tip it over," he added, "and then get a little of the water as it runs out." But the pitcher was too heavy for him.

He looked at the water, and was more thirsty still.

"I won't give up until I have to," he said. "There must be some way for me to get that water. I'll try to find it out."

At last he flew away. Do you think he gave it up? Not he. Wait a little, and you shall see what he did.

The Crow and The Pitcher.
By Wenceslas Hollar (1607–1677).

He came flying back with a little pebble in his mouth, and let it drop into the pitcher. Then he flew away, but soon came back again with another pebble. "They will help to bring the water up to me," he said.

Was he not a bright bird to think of such a way as that?

He went again, and again, and again. Each pebble made the water rise in the pitcher a little; each time he came, the crow tried to reach it.

"If I can drop pebbles enough, it will save my life," he said. For now he was growing faint.

The very next pebble that he dropped he could reach down and touch; and one or two more brought the water so high that he could dip his bill into it.

He drank every drop. And now he felt well and strong again. "This," he said, "is what people mean when they say,

"'If I cannot find a way, I will make one.'"

ÆSOP.

Hans Christian Andersen.
By Constantin Hansen, 1836.

THIRD WEEK OF JUNE.

WE have another story, written for the children, by a man of whom you have been told.

You have heard many of his stories, but not the half he has written. You will hear many more of them, and perhaps read them for yourselves in public school. This man was born in the city of Odense, Denmark.

[The teacher may give points until the children guess Hans Andersen, after which the story of The Ugly Duckling may be told. Staff and Ring Story may be told.]

A STORY FOR THE LESSONS WITH STAFFS AND RINGS.

On a hill-top there once stood a very tall and beautiful pine-tree whose roots struck deep into the earth, wrapping their arms about some cold black lumps of iron.

[Draw, or, better than doing it yourself, encourage the children to draw, a hill with a tree upon it.]

The black lumps of iron knew nothing of the sunshine and rain, the flowers and the children, except what the rootlets of the pine-tree whispered; the rootlets heard it from their cousins, the pine needles, who speak a strange language understood by few people. Little children can hear more of the talk between the leaves and flowers than can grown people, I suppose.

These little roots loved the iron, and were sorry it could get no news from the sun-land except what they might bring; you would have been very happy to see the rootlets clasp the rough iron with their tiny fingers while they whispered pretty secrets about the coming of the rain, or the play of the sunshine over their heads.

One day a woodman came with an axe to cut down the pine-tree, for a new use had been found for it.

[The man with the axe may be drawn, the children singing "Little workmen are chopping."]

Ancient Mine Work Near Bream.

From *Iron Making in the Olden Times*, by H. G. Nicholls, 1866.

Happily a wise man came for the iron too.

[Another man may be drawn, with shovel or pick, coming from the opposite side of the tree.]

The pine-tree was cut down, and the lumps of iron were dug out of the ground, but neither the pine-tree, nor its little roots, nor the lumps of iron felt the least sad or unhappy, for they were going on a journey, though they did not expect to go to the same place.

The woodman cut the pine-tree down and took it to a mill, where it was sawed into tiny bits which were made smooth and pretty, some pieces as short as a baby's thumb, some pieces as long as mamma's finger, and some as long as grandmamma's knitting-needles. The pine-tree was very happy to be made into such pretty smooth pieces, and to be wrapped in neat little bundles, all marked with a new name, which you shall hear by and by, after we go to find the lumps of iron that lived — where?

[Question children as to where it lived and who came for it.]

The cold, black lumps of iron were dug out of the ground and put in a great furnace fire, which heated the iron all through, until it glowed like the fire itself, and became as soft and yielding as the clay you sometimes make into balls and apples. While the iron was hot and soft, it was made into steel rings, which were put in boxes and sent to Boston, where they were laid on the very same shelf, in the very same store, with the bundles of little pine sticks that were now named *staffs*.

One day I went to that store and bought this box — hear the rings jingle—and this little bundle — see the staffs dance when I take off the rubber — and brought them here for you; and you will learn to make a great many pretty forms with the straight pine staffs and the round steel rings, — after the iron is heated and pounded so much, it is called steel, — and I am sure you will never forget that the pine-tree grows up in the sunshine, and the iron is found down in the ground.

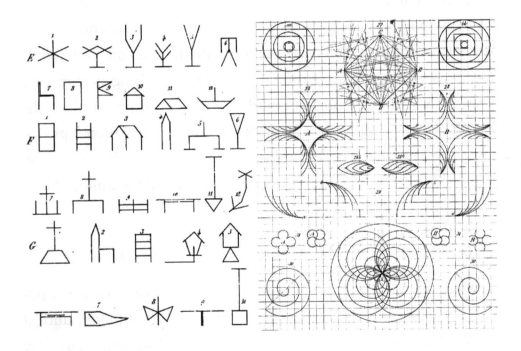

Images from *Manuel Pratique Des Jardins D'Enfants* by Frederic Froebel 1860
"...and you will learn to make a great many pretty forms with
the straight pine staffs and the round steel rings."

THE UGLY DUCKLING.

It was so beautiful in the country! It was the summer time. The wheat-fields were golden, the oats were green, and the hay stood in great stacks in the green meadows. Yes, it was beautiful, it was delightful in the country.

In a sunny spot stood a pleasant old farmhouse; and from the walls down to the water's edge grew great burdocks, so high that under the tallest of them a little child might stand upright. The spot was as wild as if it had been in the very centre of the thick wood.

Here sat a duck upon her nest, watching for her young brood to hatch; she had begun to think it a wearisome task, for the little ones were so long coming out of their shells, and she seldom had visitors.

At length, however, one shell cracked, and soon another; and from each came a living creature, that lifted its head and cried, "Peep, peep!"

"Quack, quack!" said the mother; and then they all tried to say it, too, as well as they could, as they looked all about them on every side at the tall green leaves. Their mother allowed them to look about as much as they liked, because green is good for the eyes.

"What a great world it is, to be sure," said the little ones, when they found how much more room they had than when they were in the egg-shell.

"There's one egg that takes a deal of hatching.
The shell is hard and will not break,"
From *Quacks: The Story of the Ugly Duckling, After Hans Christian Andersen*
by Marion M. Wingrave, 1884.

"Do you imagine this is the whole of the world?" said the mother. "Wait till you have seen the garden. Far beyond that it stretches down to the pastor's field, though I have never ventured to such a distance. Are you all out?"

"No, not all; the largest egg lies there yet."

"I'm really beginning to be tired;" but for all that she sat down again.

"Well, and how are you today?" quacked an old duck, who came to pay her a visit.

"There's one egg that takes a deal of hatching. The shell is hard and will not break," said the fond mother, who sat still upon her nest.

"But just look at the others. Have I not a pretty family? Are they not the prettiest little ducks you ever saw?"

"Let me see the egg that will not break," said the old duck. "Take my advice and leave it where it is. Come to the water, and teach the other children to swim."

"I think I will sit a little longer," said the mother; "I have sat so long, a day or two will not matter."

"Very well, please yourself," said the old duck, rising; and she went away.

At last the great egg broke, and the latest bird cried "Peep, peep!" as he crept forth from the shell. How big and ugly he was! The mother duck stared at him and did not know what to think. "Really," she said, "this is an enormous duckling, and it is not at all like any of the others."

On the next day the weather was delightful. The sun shone brightly on the green burdock-leaves, and the mother duck took her whole family down to the water, and jumped in with a splash. "Quack, quack!" cried she, and one after another the little ducks jumped in. The water closed over their heads, but they came up again in an instant, and swam about with their legs paddling under them as easily as possible; and the ugly gray-coat was in the water, swimming with them.

"Oh," said the mother, "see how well he uses his legs, and how erect he holds himself! He is my own child, and he is not so very ugly after all, if you look at him properly. Quack, quack! come with me to the farmyard. Come, now, don't turn in your toes; a well-bred duckling spreads his feet wide apart, just like his father and mother, in this way; now bend your necks and say 'Quack.'"

The ducklings did as they were bade; but the other ducks stared, and said, "Look, here comes another brood, and what a queer-looking object one of them is; we don't want him here;" and then one flew out and bit him in the neck.

"...was pushed and made fun of by all the poultry."
Illustration by Vilhelm Pedersen (1820-1859).
From *The Children's Book* by Horace Elisha Scudder, 1881.

"Let him alone," said the mother; "he is not doing any harm."

"Yes, but he is so big and ugly. He's a perfect fright," said the spiteful duck, "and therefore he must be turned out."

"The others are very pretty children," said an old duck, "all but that one. I wish his mother could smooth him up a bit; he is really ill-favored."

"That is impossible, your grace," replied the mother. "He is not pretty, but he has a very good disposition, and swims as well or even better than the others. He has remained too long in the egg, and therefore his figure is not properly formed;" and then she stroked his neck and smoothed the feathers.

"The other ducklings are graceful enough," said the old duck. "Now make yourself at home."

And so they made themselves comfortable; but the poor duckling who had crept out of his shell last of all, and looked so ugly, was pushed and made fun of by all the poultry.

"He is too big," they said; and the turkey cock, who had been born into the world with spurs, and fancied himself really an emperor, puffed himself out like a vessel under full sail, and flew at the duckling. He became quite red in the head with anger, so that the poor little thing did not know where to go, and was quite miserable because he was so ugly as to be laughed at by the whole farmyard.

So it went on from day to day. The poor duckling was driven about by every one; even his brothers and sisters were unkind to him, and would say, "Ah, you ugly creature!" So at last he ran away, frightening the little birds in the hedge as he flew over the palings. "They are afraid of me, too, because I am so ugly," he said. So he closed his eyes and flew still faster, until he came out on a large moor, inhabited by wild ducks. Here he remained the whole night, feeling very tired and

"Here, in this cottage, lived a woman, a cat, and a hen."
Illustration by Vilhelm Pedersen (1820-1859).
From *The Children's Book* by Horace Elisha Scudder, 1881.

sorrowful. In the morning when the wild ducks rose in the air, they stared at their new comrade. "What sort of a duck are you?" they all said, coming round him.

He bowed to them, and was as polite as he could be; but he did not reply to their question. "You are exceedingly ugly," said the wild ducks; "but that will not matter if you are polite."

After he had been on the moor two days, there came two wild geese.

"Listen, friend," said one of them to the duckling; "you are so ugly that we like you very well. Will you go with us? Not far from here is another moor and you may make your fortune, ugly as you are."

He waited quietly for several hours, and then, after looking carefully around him, hastened away from the moor as fast as he could. He ran over field and meadow till a storm arose, and he could hardly struggle against it.

Towards evening he reached a poor little cottage into which he crept.

Here, in this cottage, lived a woman, a cat, and a hen. The cat, whom his mistress called "My little son," was a great favorite; he could raise his back, and purr, and could even throw out sparks from his fur if it were stroked the wrong way. The hen had very short legs; so she was called "Chickie Short-legs." She laid good eggs, and her mistress loved her as if she had been her own child.

In the morning, when the strange visitor was discovered, the cat began to purr and the hen to cluck. "What is that noise about?" said the old woman, looking around the room; but her sight was not very good, therefore, when she saw the duckling, she thought it must be a fat duck that had strayed from home. "Oh, what a prize!" she exclaimed. "Perhaps I shall have some duck's eggs; I must wait and see." So the duckling was allowed to remain on trial for three weeks; but there were no eggs.

Now the cat was the master of the house, and the hen was the mistress; and they always said, "We and the world," for they believed themselves to be half the world, and by far the better half, too.

"Can you lay eggs?" asked the hen.

"No."

"Then have the goodness to cease talking."

"Can you raise your back, or purr, or throw out sparks?" said the cat.

"No."

"Then you have no right to express an opinion when sensible people are speaking." So the duckling sat in a corner, feeling very low-spirited; but when the sunshine and the fresh air came into the room through the open door, he began to feel such a great longing for a swim on the water, that he could not help speaking of it.

"What an absurd idea," said the hen. "You have nothing else to do, therefore you have foolish fancies. If you could purr or lay eggs they would pass away."

"But it is so delightful to swim about on the water;" said the duckling, "and so refreshing to feel it close over your head, while you dive down to the bottom."

"Delightful, indeed! it must be a queer sort of pleasure," said the hen. "Why, you must be crazy! Ask the cat, — he is the cleverest animal I know, — ask him how he would like to swim about on the water, or to dive under it, for I will not speak of my own opinion. Ask our mistress, the old woman; there is no one in the world more clever than she is. Do you think she would relish swimming, and letting the water close over her head? "

"I see you don't understand me," said the duckling.

"We don't understand you? Who can understand you, I wonder? Do you consider yourself more clever than the cat or the old woman? I will say nothing of myself. Don't imagine such nonsense, child, and thank your good fortune that you have been so well received here. Are you not in a warm room, and in society from which you may learn something? But you are a chatterer, and your company is not very agreeable. Believe me, I speak only for your good. I may tell you unpleasant truths, but that is a proof of my friendship. I advise you, therefore, to lay eggs and learn to purr as quickly as possible."

"I believe I must go out into the world again," said the duckling.

"Yes, do," said the hen. So the duckling left the cottage, and soon found water on which it could swim and dive; but he was avoided by all other animals, because of his ugly appearance.

Autumn came, and the leaves in the forest turned to orange and gold; then, as winter approached, the wind caught them as they fell, and whirled them in the cold air. The clouds, heavy with hail and snowflakes, hung low in the sky, and the raven stood on the ferns, crying, "Croak, croak!" It made one shiver with cold to look at him. All this was very sad for the poor duckling.

One evening, just as the sun was setting amid radiant clouds, there came a large flock of beautiful birds out of the bushes. The duckling had never seen any like them before. They were swans; and they curved their beautiful necks, while their soft plumage shone with dazzling whiteness. They uttered a singular cry, as they spread their glorious wings and flew away from those cold regions to warmer countries across the sea. As they mounted higher and higher in the air, the ugly little duckling felt quite a strange sensation as he watched them. He whirled himself in the water like a wheel, stretched out his neck toward them, and uttered a cry so strange that it frightened even himself. Could he ever forget those beautiful, happy birds! And when at last they were out of his sight, he dived under the water, and rose again almost beside himself with excitement. He knew not the names of these birds, nor where they had flown; but he felt towards them as he had never felt for any other bird in the world. He was not envious of these beautiful creatures; it never occurred to him to wish to be as lovely as they. Poor ugly creature, how gladly he would have lived even with the ducks, had they only given him encouragement. The water grew colder and colder; he was obliged to swim about in the water to keep it from freezing; but every night the space on which he swam grew smaller and smaller. At length it froze so hard that the ice in the water crackled as he moved, and the duckling had to paddle with his legs as well as he could to keep the space from closing up. He became exhausted at last, and lay still and helpless, frozen fast in the snow.

Early in the morning a peasant, who was passing by, saw what had happened. He broke the ice with his wooden shoe, and carried the duckling home to his wife. The warmth revived the poor little creature; but when the children wanted to play with him, the duckling thought they would do him some harm, so he started up in terror, fluttered into the milk-pan and splashed the milk about the room. Then the woman clapped her hands, which frightened him still more. He flew first into the butter-cask, then into the meal-tub, and out again. What a condition he was in! The woman screamed, and struck at him with the tongs; the children laughed and screamed and tumbled over each other, in their efforts to catch him; but luckily he escaped. The door stood open; the poor creature could just manage to slip out among the bushes, and lie down quite exhausted in the newly-fallen snow.

It would be very sad were I to relate all the misery and privations which the poor little duck endured during the hard winter; but when it had passed, he found himself lying one morning in a moor, amongst the rushes. He felt the warm sun shining, and heard the lark singing, and saw that all around was beautiful spring.

Then the young bird felt that his wings were strong, as he flapped them against his sides, and rose high into the air. They bore him onwards until he found himself in a large garden, before he well knew how it had happened. The apple-trees were in full blossom, and the fragrant elders bent their long green branches down to the stream which wound round a smooth lawn. Everything looked beautiful. From a thicket close by came three white swans, rustling their feathers, and swimming lightly over the smooth water. The duckling remembered the beautiful birds, and felt more unhappy than ever.

"I will fly to those royal birds!" he exclaimed, "and they will kill me because, ugly as I am, I dare to go near them. Better be killed by them than pecked by ducks, beaten by hens, or starved with hunger in the winter." Then he flew to the water and swam towards the beautiful swans. The moment they saw the stranger they rushed to meet him with outspread wings.

"Kill me," said the poor bird, and he bent his head down to the surface of the water.

But what did he see in the clear stream? His own image; no longer a dark gray bird, ugly to look at, but a graceful and snowy swan.

"...what did he see ... a graceful and snowy swan."
Illustration by Vilhelm Pedersen (1820-1859).
From *The Children's Book* by Horace Elisha Scudder, 1881.

To be born in a duck's nest, in a farmyard, is of no consequence to a bird, if it is hatched from a swan's egg. He now felt glad at having suffered sorrow and trouble, because it enabled him to enjoy so much better all the pleasure and happiness around him; for the great swans swam round the new-comer, and stroked his neck with their beaks, as a welcome.

Into the garden presently came some little children, and threw bread and cake into the water.

"See," cried the youngest, "there is a new one;" and the rest were delighted, and ran to their father and mother, dancing and clapping their hands, and shouting joyously, "There is another swan come; a new one has arrived."

Then they threw more bread and cake into the water, and said, "The new one is the most beautiful of all; he is so young and pretty." And the old swans bowed their heads before him.

Then he felt quite ashamed, and hid his head under his wing; for he did not know what to do, he was so happy; yet he was not at all proud. He had been persecuted and despised for his ugliness, and now he heard them say he was the most beautiful of all the birds. Even the elder tree bent down its boughs into the water before him, and the sun shone warm and bright. Then he rustled his feathers, curved his slender neck, and cried joyfully, from the depths of his heart, "I never dreamed of such happiness as this while I was the despised ugly duckling."

ANDERSEN.

WE THANK THEE.

For flowers that bloom about our feet;
For tender grass, so fresh, so sweet;
For song of bird and hum of bee;
For all things fair we hear or see, —
Father in heaven, we thank thee!

For blue of stream and blue of sky;
For pleasant shade of branches high;
For fragrant air and cooling breeze;
For beauty of the blooming trees,—
Father in heaven, we thank thee!

For mother-love and father-care,
For brothers strong and sisters fair;
For love at home and here each day;
For guidance, lest we go astray, —
Father in heaven, we thank thee!

ANONYMOUS.

Black Bear Foraging.

1905.

A TRUE BEAR STORY.

A farmer once lived a long way from town; he raised potatoes on his farm, corn for his meal, wheat for his flour, cows to supply him with milk and butter, and hens to lay eggs for his breakfast. He had to buy his sugar and salt, coffee and rice in the village.

One day late in autumn he took some potatoes and wheat to town to sell, and he bought some sugar and rice to take to his children. He bought a large quantity of sugar which he took home in a small barrel in the back of his wagon. When he was driving through the woods, just as they were approaching a bridge, the horses stopped in the road and stood on their hind legs. You may be sure the farmer was surprised, and, as the horses refused to go on, he gave the reins to his wife and got out to see what was the matter; it was almost dark, so the farmer could not see very plainly, but he could see something black on the bridge, and on going a little nearer, he saw that it was a large black bear, standing on his hind legs, that had frightened the horses; the farmer was not much afraid, and he snapped his whip at the bear, and made him jump from the bridge, and run away; then the farmer got into his wagon again and started homeward; but he had not driven far before he heard a low growling behind him, and there was the bear in the back of the wagon, with his nose in the sugar barrel. The farmer's wife was very much afraid of the bear, but the farmer told her not to fear as it was sugar the bear wanted, and again the farmer drove the bear away by snapping his whip and shouting. Then he said perhaps the little bears would like a taste of sugar, and he would make sure that the bear would not follow them home and into the pantry, which he did by throwing a pound of the sugar out into the road where the bears could get it.

Black Bear.

From *Our Big Game: A Book For Sportsmen And Nature Lovers*

By Dwight Williams Huntington, 1904.

CARDAMOM
PUBLISHERS

CPSIA information can be obtained
at www.ICGtesting.com
Printed in the USA
BVHW010534210921
617180BV00007B/165

9 780974 218144